# GOD IN CREATION AND EVOLUTION

# GOD IN CREATION AND EVOLUTION

*A. Hulsbosch,* O. S. A.

*translated by Martin Versfeld*

*Sheed and Ward : : New York*

Originally published as *De Schepping Gods,* Roermond and Maaseik, J. J. Romen & Zonen, 1963.

This book is published in England under the title *God's Creation*.

NIHIL OBSTAT: ANDREAS J. MOORE, L.C.L. CENSOR DEPUTATUS

IMPRIMATUR ✠ PATRITIUS CASEY, VIC. GEN.

WESTMONASTERII, DIE 26 JANUARII 1965

The *Nihil obstat* and *Imprimatur* are a declaration that a book or pamphlet is considered to be free from doctrinal or moral error. It is not implied that those who have granted the *Nihi obstat* and *Imprimatur* agree with the contents, opinions or statements expressed.

Library of Congress Catalog Card Number 66-12268

Manufactured in the United States of America

# CONTENTS

# INTRODUCTION

The sciences, in investigating the past of the cosmos and of the earth, confront great riddles, yet the fact that evolution has occurred and is occurring can no longer be denied. By evolution I mean more particularly the coming into being of our planet as it now is from a mysterious primal condition several milliard years in the past. This occurs by way of the formation of the elements and of ever more complicated chemical structures; and then of the formation of vegetable and animal life, until the human phase is arrived at. We can no longer deny that, on the biological side, man originates in the animal kingdom.

In this way an image of the world is revealed which we can call new with as much right as we call new the image which four hundred years ago, in scientific circles at any rate, supplanted the Ptolemaic. In our day the scientific image which came in with Copernicus and others has been not supplanted but implemented. It has acquired a new dimension. This new dimension is at the same time the correction of an aspect which that scientific image had taken over from the Ptolemaic, namely, the ascription of a static character to the cosmic order. In this respect the evolutionary image stands in contrast with the old representation. Previously man did not reckon with the fact that the world and humanity were journeying to a future as mysterious as their point of departure.

The history of human thought, until the dawn of the new period, displays various conceptions of the structuring of the cosmos. These can all be described as primitive, because perfected methods of observation and of insight into the laws of nature, necessary for a well-founded judgment, were lacking. The irruption of the Copernican image had upsetting effects among the theologians, and we all know that in that troubled time the Holy Office took up a reactionary position. Yet we should not judge too harshly, since we can hardly imagine what it then meant to hear that the heavens overhead were not really there. From the beginning of the history of revelation until then, a more or less constant image of the world was the vehicle of divine revelation, and it need hardly surprise us that the mutual relationship between man's image and God's revelation was not immediately comprehended.

Among theologians it gradually became apparent that the primitive image, which was assumed in the interpretation of revelation, did not share in the infallibility of the revelation, but was a human factor capable of improvement. In the encyclical *Providentissimus Deus* of 1893, Leo XIII wrote that no real conflict between the theologian and the physicist could arise while both observed the limits of their respective sciences. The sacred writers, or better, the Spirit of God, who spoke through them, did not intend to teach men concerning the internal structure of visible things, the knowledge of which contributes nothing to salvation. This papal announcement marked the beginning of the end of a centuries-long conflict.

Yet the sciences reaped the immediate profit, the Church drew no closer to the world. The words of Leo XIII are in principle entirely justified; this scientific partition of estates can only be profitable to both parties. But the theologian had better not think that he has now done with the matter. He had better not think that he can dispense with an image of the cosmos, or, even worse, that he can carry on with an image which has had its day. For he will then be trying to announce God's work of salvation in a language strange to his public. In this lies one of the main reasons why contemporary preaching comes across so poorly to the faithful, and why many non-believers expect a speedy liquidation of Christianity.

Preaching cannot dispense with a contemporary picture of the world. If it uses either no picture, or the pieces of one which is antiquated, then it will seem to the hearers either to be talking abstractions or to be saying nothing at all. The world to come holds the interest of theologians, but who can speak about it in a way which really stimulates the listener? Perhaps the theologian has never thought so much, and the average Christian so little, about the last things as today. Preaching impresses the hearers as coming from another world, from which they are excluded. Even where the message of the Word is still accepted, it can be integrated into life only with difficulty. Everywhere, people are seeking for the Christian meaning of labour, of technics, of the practice of science, and of all the other concerns of modern man. It is here that we feel the vacuum which has grown in the course of centuries, as a consequence of theology's losing fruitful contact with the universe as men have come to know it.

If you were to ask a Christian what positive connection there is between Christ's death on the cross and the evolution of life on earth, he would presumably shrug his shoulders at so nonsensical a question, or possibly consider it a profanation to connect the sacrifice of Jesus with evolution. Jesus' death on the cross is a matter of revelation, evolution a matter of science. The shrug or the shock is a symptom of the fact that the Christian frequently does not even feel it to be a loss that he should speak about the cross of Christ without connecting it with an image of the world. It is striking how the Apostles, especially St. Paul, had, within a few decades after the death of Jesus, integrated the current image of the world into their preaching of Jesus' death and resurrection. The letters to the Ephesians and the Colossians are a beautiful example of this.

We ought thus to realize clearly that the declaration of Leo XIII is a first step, which has necessarily to be followed by a second, which is the preaching of revelation with the help of the modern image. So far practically nothing has been done. In the meanwhile we have transferred from a static scientific image of the world to an evolutionary one, and the danger exists that preaching is progressively losing contact with contemporary people. The evolutionary image has inherited all the advantages of its predecessor. On this account theology will perform a great task if it fully assimilates into its teaching evolution and all the connected facets of cosmic reality.

We must not make the same mistake as the theologians who made things so difficult for Galileo. Those are surely wrong who say that we cannot assume an image which has not been fully worked out and demonstrated by science. It is true that science still confronts many problems, but we can hardly doubt the fact of evolution. The popularizing of the modern image proceeds apace, owing to cheap books, the radio, and television. Nowadays, everybody knows something about evolution. Questions about Adam and Eve and original sin come up. Priests must know how to treat them when catechizing.

Although the new image is not established in detail, we cannot refuse to accept it. The Bible makes use of an image which can be called fitting only in a limited sense. That there is a kingdom of death beneath the earth, and that there is a mass of water above the firmament is taken for granted by the biblical writers. They know only the great luminary (the sun), the lesser luminary (the moon), and the stars, all fastened to the arch of heaven. The earth rests on pillars, standing in the primeval sea. However primitive and inexact these representations may have been, they played their part in the announcement of God's creative power.

We ought to take the findings of science seriously. They are helping to produce a new image of the world—that is, a new way of regarding the structure of cosmic reality. Arising from this new insight come doubts about the truth of what the Church teaches, because it is not granted to everybody to be able to distinguish between revealed truth and the dress in which it is presented. We say nowadays: If only the earlier theologians had listened to the astronomers! But what happened or did not happen in the past should call our attention to the possibility that the sciences may have something to tell us now. If the Church's formulations show elements which conflict with the generally accepted findings of science, we should no longer hesitate to look for new formulations *while preserving the full content of the dogma.* Given that theology has not assimilated the modern image into its system and influenced the official declarations of doctrine of the Church along this channel, the formulations in question are perhaps more susceptible of change than they appear.

It is of course easier for the theologian to repeat what has always been said, but necessity compels him to correct his language. The easy way of repetition looks like fidelity to the traditional teaching of the Church, but it can in fact be the cause of the lapse of many. The answer to the question, what can remain and what should be changed, is a matter requiring great prudence. Anybody who ventures an answer must often ask himself whether what he says is well founded. When efforts succeed, the theologian will experience a rich reward for his trouble, since he will be speaking an intelligible language once more. In this way a fruitful reciprocity between theology and science can come into being, and it is pleasing to note that this is happening here and there.

In my effort to assimilate the evolutionary image to my teaching of what revelation says about creation, sin, and redemption, I have frequently been astonished by the way in which Holy Scripture shows its divine inspiration almost visibly. Naturally, I do not wish to suggest that, in some occult way or other, evolution is spoken of in Holy Scripture. But the teaching of the Bible comes to life in unexpected ways when we know of evolution.

In retrospect this is understandable, when we consider that in the Bible we have to do with a history of salvation. We are concerned with the *history* of God's intercourse with his people, and that is why it has an essential relationship with the *history* of God's creation. The whole work of creation is orientated from the beginning to its consummation in the history of salvation. It is properly and in fact *one* history. Without knowing the evolutionary image, the Bible tells the story of the last two phases of evolution. It tells of man now, and of man to come. This is how we can really see it, now that we have a better insight into the history of the cosmos. The last phase of evolution is introduced by the redemptive work of Christ. Easter is the feast of feasts, the day on which the creation of man in Christ reaches its consummation.

The writing of this book has been much facilitated by my having in the past been occupied with the biblical theology of creation and redemption. The theology of creation must be looked for particularly in the Sapiential literature. To this belong, first, the so-called Sapiential books, one part of which belong to the deutero-canonical, or in another nomenclature, to the pseudo-epigraphic writings. The Book of Wisdom (or, to give it its fuller title, the Wisdom of Solomon) has come to be seen as very important for our purpose, because on the one hand it continues the tradition of Israel, and, on the other, shows considerable affinity with Johannine and Pauline theology.

The Sapiential literature represents a literary *genre* which is not confined to the Sapiential books in the strict sense but has also left its traces in certain passages in the Prophets. Further, it would not be difficult to show affinities between the theology of the Hebrew Wisdom writers and those of Deuteronomy.

The subjects which come under discussion in the confrontation of current theology with scientific insight into the history of the earth and its forms of life necessarily concern especially the beginning and the end: original sin and eschatology. Naturally I had not completed the task. There are many mists which this book does not disperse. But I hope that it will be an incitement to others to apply themselves to these difficult questions.

It would not be right to conclude these introductory remarks without mention of a man by whom, to a high degree, I have been inspired: Pierre Teilhard de Chardin, S.J. In my exposition I have not been concerned with criticism of specific aspects of his great conception. Others have done that competently. Thus we have the thorough study by Dr. P. Smulders, S.J., *Het visioen van Teilhard de Chardin* (1962). This meets the need of making some of his theological statements more precise and correct.

The name of Teilhard is scarcely mentioned in this book. Yet without his example it would probably not have been written. Although Teilhard was no professional theologian, he nevertheless did what the theologians had not done: he was the first after the rise of the natural sciences to speak about God and Christ in terms of the scientific image. That is his immortal merit, which has perhaps not yet been sufficiently admitted. I should consider it a great honour were these pages regarded as a tribute to the memory of this pioneer who, on Easter 1955, went to the vision of his Creator.

A. H.

*Feast of the Epiphany, 1963*

# I

# TWO PHASES OF EVOLUTION

According to a well-known definition of the First Vatican Council, the Church of God holds and teaches that the origin and purpose of all things can be known with certainty from the study of creatures *by the natural light of human reason.* Thanks to divine revelation, the Council continues, those divine truths which in themselves are not accessible to human reason can also be known by all without hindrance, with certainty, and without admixture of error, even in the present condition of human nature.

The first statement contains a reflection of a passage from the *Summa* of St. Thomas, where he says that "the truth about God, as pursued by reason, can be attained by few persons, after the expenditure of much time, and mixed with many errors." (1, q. 1, art. 1.) The Council expresses itself less strongly than St. Thomas. What strikes one is the omission of the words "by few persons, after the expenditure of much time."

The words of St. Thomas seem strange when we compare

them with what St. Paul says in Rom. i.18-21: "For the wrath of God is revealed from heaven against all ungodliness and wickedness of men who by their wickedness suppress the truth. For what can be known about God is plain to them because God has shown it to them. Ever since the creation of the world his invisible nature, namely, his eternal power and deity, has been clearly perceived in the things that have been made. So they are without excuse; for although they knew God they did not honour him as God or give thanks to him, but they became futile in their thinking and their senseless minds were darkened."

Here it is said that the pagans in fact all have a knowledge of God from creation, but that they suppress this truth because of their unrighteousness. As the sequel shows, the sin of the pagans is idolatry and the confusion of morals to which it leads. It was not *some* pagans that knew God, for the reproach touches all idolaters.

The author of the Book of Wisdom says the same thing more fully, and in a terminology more philosophically coloured. Of exceptional interest is xiii.1-5: "For all men who were ignorant of God were foolish by nature: they were unable from the good things that are seen to know him who exists, nor did they recognize the craftsman while paying heed to his works . . . For from the greatness and beauty of created things comes a corresponding perception of the creator."

The reader will notice that he is not here concerned with a proof of God's existence that can be attained by few persons after much time and mixed with many errors. One gets the impression that the demonstration of God's existence is something other than the knowledge of God spoken of in these quotations. In them we have to do with the contemplation of the invisible being of God (the paradox is St. Paul's) from his creation; with a seeing of God by all who have not suppressed the truth by ungodliness. The idolaters don't want to see what they are able to see. This may lie in their nature; that is why they are to be recognized as "foolish by nature" because of their rejection of God. What a human being can know of God was in fact known to the pagans, but though they knew God, they did not honour him. From the vastness and beauty of creation they could know their Creator by comparison.

Well, what one sees, one does not have to demonstrate rationally. One might even ask if reasoning makes sense here. I cannot establish by reasoning that the music which I hear is beautiful. It is not a question of demonstration but of hearing. Holy Scripture speaks in the same way about our knowledge of God from creation. "God himself gave them the knowledge." He himself is the beauty which greets us in creation. The universe is a genuine revelation of God, although without words.

> The heavens tell the glory of God;
> and the firmament proclaims his handiwork.
> Day to day pours forth speech
> and night to night declares knowledge.

There is no speech, nor are there words;
their voice is not heard;
yet their voice goes out through all the earth,
and their words to the end of the world.

[Ps. xix. 1-4]

For thou, O Lord, hast made me glad by thy work;
at the works of thy hands I sing for joy.
How great are thy works, O Lord!
Thy thoughts are very deep!
The dull man cannot know,
the stupid cannot understand this.

[Ps. xcii(xci).4-6]

The demonstration of God's existence leads to a result other than that of the knowledge of God of which Scripture speaks. From the proof we know that God exists, and this is something quite other than seeing him in creation.

But if Scripture speaks of a direct knowledge of God from creation, that is, of a revelation of God to those who are open to it, then we may suppose that knowledge of this revelation will be much more common than the construction of the difficult rational proof. It would also follow that the presence of God in the world must be approached differently from the way we approach it in a philosophical or theological context, where we demonstrate the existence of God either from the effects of his creative power or from his utterance. The question which here concerns us is connected, in my opinion, with two problems that intensely rouse the contemporary Christian: first, the well-known complaint that God has been driven out of the world by the natural sciences; and next, the connection of Christianity with the other world religions. Let us look at both problems.

In Wisd. xiii.1 the writer speaks of God as he who exists, whom the foolish cannot get to know from the visible world. We should be wrong if we thought that he who exists is here conceived of as a static *ens a se*. This holds also of the verb "to be" where it occurs in Wisd. i.14: "For he created all things that they might exist." The words "that they might exist" look to us like a superfluous addition. But "being" means here the unfolding of life, the coming to a fully actualized existence. "The existent" is thought of not statically but dynamically. The creation is the creaturely translation of this existing. God makes his appearance, becomes visible in creation in a hidden way.

The rational proof appears to me to be connected with a dualistic conception of man, to which a dualistic approach to the cosmos corresponds. The soul of man is no longer wholly in the body. The soul can do a great deal without the body; for instance, demonstrate the existence of God from creation. The God whom we reach in this way is elevated to a height unconnected with creatures, and is related in the thought of the philosopher *to* the creation, but is no longer *in* creation seen as the veiled manifestation of his invisible being. The connection between God and creation is established by means of the principle of causality. Then you have a cosmos, to which the body and the visible world belong, and a soul which knows that God exists. But the whole *man* does not know, as the soul does, that God is present in the visible creation. There is a sense in which God and the soul have been detached from the visible world. Isn't this the real root of that absence of God about which we talk so much nowadays? If we are to find God in the world again, shall we not have to revise our conception of man?

At this point one thinks of existential phenomenology which, like the Bible, is thoroughly in earnest about the unity of man, and regards him as a subject existing in a bodily mode. The appearance of the human spirit is thus correlative with the appearance of God in the sense of the revelation of God in creation. Just as the human spirit is not identical with the body, but nevertheless expresses itself in the body, so God transcends creation, though this does not minimize the fact that he expresses himself in creation. Man is made in the image of God, and prepared by God for a dialogue with him; and yet this dialogue is not carried on by the soul with a God placed outside creation, but by a man with God revealing himself in creation. The human spirit expresses itself in the body, and that is why God is known by man, as incorporated subject, in his revelation through creation. Both partners in the dialogue are, each in his own way, incarnate. The expression of God in creation confronts the regard of a man whose spirit makes its appearance in his corporality. There is a complete correlation here, and the penetration of this correlation will constantly be necessary to build our theology of evolution on the Bible, because this is how the Bible thinks. From beginning to end it has God appearing and revealing himself through and in creation.

More audibly than the proofs of God's existence, St. Thomas addresses us through another side of his teaching, namely, in his lovely vision of the natural longing of Man to behold God. According to St. Thomas this longing is of the essence of man. It is given naturally though it cannot be realized without grace. When we apply this vision to what Scripture says about the knowledge of God from creation, we see that this knowledge, if it is reached, cannot be separated in thought from grace. Man's nature points to this knowledge, but the actualizing of our natural knowledge of God is never without grace.

According to the First Vatican Council, the Church holds and teaches that God can be known with certainty by the natural light of reason when it regards creatures. This does not contradict what we have just said. On the contrary, it would appear that there is more locked up in this statement than the theologians have got out of it. Though it be true that in fact the actualization of our knowledge of God from nature cannot take place without grace, it remains true that the knowledge which earthly man has of God is tied to his natural mode of knowledge, which is determined by his terrestrial existence. It belongs to the essence of earthly man that he should have a knowledge of God from visible things by the natural light which is in him. That is why he can be spoken to by revelation.

We can therefore assume that this knowledge of God is found everywhere on earth, given that the inward eye is clear; that is, given that the truth is not suppressed by idolatry; or, in more modern language, given that men do not think that this world can satisfy man. That is why all religions, in which the human heart seeks a supramundane perfection, possess the truth, but not the unclouded truth, where the certain assurance of revelation is lacking, and there are additions of error. This offers an open prospect for a dialogue between the Church and the world religions. The Logos enlightens *every* man. (John i.9.)

The text of Rom. i.18-21 tells ultimately of the innate capacity of man to know God from creatures, and in the same way as Rom. ii.12-16 speaks of the innate knowledge of the moral law. According to St. Thomas this capacity implies at the same time the longing to see the Maker of creation. This connection between the perception of God in the veiled revelation of his creation and the natural desire for the sight of God constitutes the natural order as a territory on its own, which has validity as long as man dwells on earth. In the future another way of being human will dawn for us, which, seen from our side, we regard as belonging to a supernatural order. There, there will be a parallel connection, consisting of another way of being human and another way of knowing God in creation. The longing will then be satisfied. I shall discuss this in the chapter about the sight of God.

The two consecutive phases of the natural and of the supernatural orders are described by St. Paul in 1 Cor. xv.42-9, both in their distinctness and in their unity. In this passage the Apostle answers the question of some Corinthians as to what sort of body we shall have after the resurrection. They were casting doubts upon the possibility of the resurrection. In the first part of his answer Paul calls attention to what we should call nowadays the numerous forms in which matter can appear. He notices this variety in the stages of botanical development. First you have the seed and then the stem. But creatures also differ among one another; there is the flesh of men, of cattle, of birds and of fishes. There are heavenly bodies and terrestrial bodies, and the heavenly bodies differ from one another in splendour. Why, then, should it not be possible that humanity now, and the humanity of the future, should be corporeal in different ways? This thought is developed in *vv.*42-9. "So is it with the resurrection of the dead. What is sown is perishable, what is raised is imperishable. It is sown in dishonour, it is raised in glory. It is sown in weakness, it is raised in power. It is sown a physical body, it is raised a spiritual body. If there is a physical body, there is also a spiritual body. Thus it is written, 'The first man Adam became a living being'; the last Adam became a life-giving spirit. But it is not the spiritual which is first but the physical, and then the spiritual. The first man was from the earth, a man of dust; the second man is from heaven. As was the man of dust, so are those who are of the dust; and as is the man of heaven, so are those who are of heaven. Just as we have borne the image of the man of dust, we shall also bear the image of the man of heaven."

Here two ways of existing are clearly distinguished: a natural and a spiritual body—that is, a body animated by the psyche, or natural principle of life, and a body animated by the Spirit of God. The same distinction returns in the terms, "man of dust," and "heavenly man." We can talk here simply of the natural and supernatural orders. When mention is made of "body" it implies the whole man, in respect of his bodily mode of existence. Paul also moves from the term "body" to the term "man." In the qualificaions "perishable," "trifling," "weak," "natural," it is not the dead body that is indicated, but the living body of dust. The body in which we are now clothed is what is laid in the grave.

We should also notice that the earthly mode of Adam's existence is deduced from what he was at the moment of creation. The Fall is not brought into consideration. Adam was earthly at his creation, and natural in contrast with the mode of existence of the glorified Lord. The natural mode of existence is still referred to in *v.* 50 as "flesh and blood."

We are saying too little when we put it that earthly bodiliness belongs to the natural order. It is the expression of the natural order. If we are serious about the unity of embodied man, then we have to say that human existence in this world is radically marked by natural corporeality. All the actions of man, including his spiritual activities, bear the seal of earthly corporeality. The activity of man is, in the strictest sense, *one,* that of a soul-body. It is in this manner that man belongs in the world. It is through his bodiliness that he has a solidarity with the world and impresses the character of his humanity upon his surroundings. Earthly things are not accessible to man, except by way of his human being. His presence humanizes the world. If we maintain that the bodiliness of man is a strictly natural category, then it follows that the total existence of man in the world must be referred to this strictly natural category. The natural order has its own inviolability, while man has not been glorified with Christ. This inviolability extends over man, in his work of creating a world to live in.

The natural longing to see God is equally an aspect of the natural order and of our terrestrial bodiliness. These two aspects belong to each other. The existence of man as terrestrial bodiliness defines him as a *seeker after God.* The re-creation of man as a spiritual body defines him as *living in the vision of God.* The body of this dust separates man from the sight of God, or, to use the words of St. Paul, "flesh and blood cannot inherit the Kingdom of God." (1 Cor. xv.50.) The man of dust is in search of God, and he does this in all the activities of his humanity.

In spite of all this emphasis upon the natural order, we must not forget that, through baptism, the Christian is placed in a supernatural perspective. "He who believes, *has* eternal life." (John vi.47.) But the experience of the supernatural actuality by the Christian on earth is existentially quite different from the experience of his glorified humanity. Believing is not seeing, and hope is not possession. On the one hand, the believer is related to God by faith, hope and love, through which he has a supernatural orientation to God, but on the other hand he is signed by his bodiliness in all his thinking, willing and action. Were this not so, then faith would have passed over into sight. For the believer, too, and for him who is on the way to his supernatural goal, the terrestrial remains what it is in itself. The integrity of the natural must be extended to the totality of human existence on earth, and to the existence of the Christian as well.

Belief in God, which calls us, in Christ, to a higher destination, imports that we are summoned to this goal as the undivided subjects of a natural experience of the world. But we reach this goal when we have been re-created by God as subjects of a supernatural experience of the world. In the present life belief expresses itself in the natural desire to see God. The definition of the First Vatican Council remains valid for our whole earthly life.

Body, soul and knowledge of God hang infrangibly together. When man through Christ comes to his consummation in the immediate vision of God he must therefore change in his mode of human existence also. Man as person remains identical with himself, but this does not take away from the fact that his mode of existing reaches a higher level. Our earthly life reaches, in the future life of resurrection, not a perfection by linear projection, but an analogous actualization—man different, new, just as the immediate vision of God is something other than the earthly man's knowledge of God. The natural and the supernatural orders represent the last two phases of evolution.

# 2

# EVOLUTION AND ORIGINAL SIN

Science regards man from a biological point of view when it places him in an evolutionary series. In the following survey of human evolution this restriction must be borne in mind. Biologically considered, man belongs to the vertebrates. He is a species the fossil vestiges of which go back to thousands of centuries of the past. This seems a long time, but compared with the duration of life on earth, it lies just behind us. Although, geologically speaking, it is a recent period, the length and division of the Quaternary period is still a matter of discussion. The Diluvial occupied much the greater part of the Quaternary. It was a period of glaciation in which there was flux and reflux from cold to warm and from warm to cold. For Europe the periods of cold are generally considered to be four, and between them lie the so-called interglacials, or intervals bounded by times of glaciation. The period after the last glacial, in which we now live, is called the Alluvial. During the last glacial period but one, the glaciers of the North Pole cap extended to the middle of Holland.

To place fossil remains chronologically, one connects them with the glacial periods. As a consequence we name these periods, in terms of their duration, in thousands of years: The Günz glacial period, 600-540; the Günz-Mindel interglacial period, 540-480; the Mindel glacial period, 480-370; the Mindel-Riss interglacial, 370-240; the Riss glacial, 240-180; the Riss-Würm interglacial, 180-130; the Würm glacial, 130-10; and the Alluvial period of the last 10,000 years.

Taken all together, the remains of human fossils are very fragmentary; they are few in number and frequently consist individually of no more than a small portion of a skeleton. In the arrangement of the material I follow the zoologist Kälin, and the palaeontologist Overhage.

Both these savants distinguish three groups or circles. The point of departure for this division lies in the degree of difference in respect of the present anthropoids, gorillas, chimpanzees, and orang-outangs, which are included in the term "pongids." The difference in relation to the pongids is least sharp in (1) the Pithecanthropus group, more in (2) the Neanderthal group, and most of all in (3) the Sapiens group.

According to a theory which long had the status of a dogma this series was supposed to represent a linear descent of one form from the other. Against this ladder theory there is nowadays a fan theory, according to which the three groups have risen from a common parent stock.

(1) *The Pithecanthropus,* or *"apeman," group.* The oldest traces of the human race are found in a few widely distributed fossils (Java, Germany) which we can place approximately in the first interglacial period. The chief representatives of this group are the Pithecanthropus forms of Java and China, who seem to have existed for a long time about the middle of the Quaternary. Near Peking were found the remains of at least fifty individuals. A series of fossil remains from the North African coastal region can also be mentioned here. The variety of forms suggests that they developed in diverging directions.

(2) *The Neanderthal group.* According to the fossils this group reached its peak in the first half of the Würm glacial period. They displayed great variety, and coalesce at the end with the Sapiens group. Scientists distinguish early Neanderthalers (Rome, Gibraltar, Croatia) from those of the Riss-Würm interglacial period; Rhodesians (N.W. Rhodesia and north of Cape Town) dating from before the European Würm glacial period; and the late Neanderthalers. The latter are what we usually mean by Neanderthalers. This type was first found near Düsseldorf in 1856. Remains of about two hundred individuals were found, including a remarkable number of children. The Neanderthalers extend from Spain through France, where the greatest number of finds were made, and through Belgium, Germany and Moravia to Hungary and Italy, and on to the

Crimea and Asia Minor. The Neanderthaler displays a remarkable combination of theromorphic, or animal-like characteristics (receding forehead, prognathous jaws and projecting supraorbital crests, i.e., prominent bone formation above the eyes: reminding one of an ape); and on the other hand, human characteristics: the brain capacity exceeds that of modern man. However, one can draw no conclusions from brain capacity to intelligence. The Neanderthaler was the bearer of a well-defined Stone Age culture.

(3) *The Sapiens group.* Extending backwards from our own time, this group includes in the first place all existing humanity of all races. They are distinguished by a combination of characteristic features: the area of skull covering the brain is greater than that of the face, the forehead tends to verticality and has no supraorbital crest, the back of the head is rounded, and the chin prominent. This combination goes back to CroMagnon and Aurignacian peoples, who lived in France in the second half of the Würm period. These are preceded by the pre-Sapiens forms, which appear in the first phase of the Würm, or in the last interglacial period. They lived before, or at any rate at the same time as, the late Neanderthalers. Finds have been made principally in France (Fontéchevade). The finds in Italy, Iran, Australia and East Africa are fragmentary and hard to define. To this group belongs also Palestine Man, of whom remains were found near Mount Carmel (ten individuals), Nazareth (six individuals) and the Lake of Gennesareth (one individual). Here one discerns a mixture of characters

resembling both the Neanderthal and the Sapiens, varying in combination from individual to individual. The remains are of different dates, probably from the last interglacial to middle Würm.

I shall leave it at this summary inventory. It looks a lot, but the data are quite insufficient to give a clear picture of the fanning out of the human race during the Quaternary. There are as many hypotheses as authors. But this does not lessen the force of the fact that nowadays we can say some important things about the general line of human evolution. One can establish from the fossil remains that one cannot trace the development of man linearly, to correspond with the movement away from animal-like characteristics. It is also established that the pre-human stage of man shows more resemblance to actual men than was at first thought. This has become particularly clear from the South African finds of Australopithecids ("southern apelike"). A first find was made in 1914, but since 1938 the fossil documentation of this group has gone up to more than a hundred individuals, principally from the surroundings of Johannesburg. They show a peculiar combination of human and apelike characters. We presume that their posture in standing and walking corresponded in large measure with the human. It is a debated question whether they should be considered human. The question can only be answered by indirect indications for the existence of intelligence—culture implements, or the use of fire deducible from charcoal remains. The question remains, of course, whether techniques of this sort are in some measure possible at a pre-human level; do they require the reflexive intellect which makes man what he is?

The Australopithecid group lived more than half a million years ago and its existence at that time shows that man's line of descent had taken its own direction very long before that. In recent years this has been impressively demonstrated by finds in Italy (Tuscany), where a few years ago an almost complete skeleton was unearthed (Oropithecus). The new data enable us to trace the line of independent prehuman evolution back to a past of more than 10 million years. But it is uncertain whether these finds bring us into contact with the pre-stages of present man or with a related line which failed to sustain itself.

The conclusion of all this is: (1) The living form of man connects with a stage of pre-human forms. Man stands in the line of evolution, and in the light of contemporary scientific investigation, the genetic correspondence of the human body with pre-human forms of life cannot be dismissed. (2) The line of descent which has produced man had already followed its own course for millions of years, so that man has developed parallel to and not out of the kinds of ape. (3) The development of man, in agreement with the development of numerous other forms that have been studied, goes together with a fanning out, leading to the existence of various rather diverse forms in the same geological epoch. (4) Hope is steadily fading of finding, *on the basis of external form,* a ground for drawing a line between man and animal.

After this survey, which had to do with the place and

history of man within the framework of evolution, I shall give a short account of the ecclesiastical teaching about original sin. We have already excluded the possibility that there can be a real opposition between the conclusions of science and the dogma of the Church, because God is the source of both kinds of truth. But it is possible that the way of putting the Church's dogma and the biblical message, to which the formulations refer, has fallen behind science. In that event we shall have to restate the dogma in words that are fresh.

In its pronouncements on original sin the teaching authority of the Church has relied principally on Gen. ii-iii, and Rom. v. The main definitions of the Church are those of (1) the Council of Carthage, approved by Pope Zosimus (Denz., 101-02); (2) the Second Council of Orange, which took place a good century later and was confirmed by Pope Boniface II (Denz., 174-5); and above all (3) the Council of Trent, Fifth Session (1546), which gave precision and expansion to the teaching of the previous councils (Denz., 787-92). All these councils arrived at their definitions in answer to errors in connection with Christian grace.

The fault of Adam exercises its influence upon all his descendants. This influence, which has the character of sin, exercises its effect at the moment that a descendant of Adam comes into being, so that even for the child baptism has the significance of a sacrament for the forgiveness of sins. But original sin does not have the character of a personal sin; it is a sin which adheres to human nature as an habitual condition. Now the fact that every man born into this world is tainted with original sin is expressed by saying that original sin is transmitted to the descendants of Adam. Original sin embodies the loss of the spiritual and bodily privileges with which Adam was endowed by God. Through original sin man persists in a condition which bars his way to the sight of God, and from which he cannot free himself. His liberation is wholly to be ascribed to the grace of God in Christ Jesus.

In the description of original sin *death* occupies an important place. The Council of Carthage (Denz., 101) lays it down that death is the wages of sin: one may not say that Adam would have died whether he had sinned or not. According to the Council of Orange the fault of Adam affects his descendants not only in the death of the body, which is the punishment of sin, but also in the form of sin, which is the death of the soul and as such has been transmitted to the whole human race. (Denz., 175.) Through Adam's sin an original condition has been lost which was characterized by moral and physical integrity and was intended for the whole human race. The *whole* man is damaged in his existence by the first sin, both soul and body. (Denz., 174.) The same teaching is set out in two canons by Trent (Denz., 788f.), of which the first speaks about the person of Adam himself, and the second about the consequences which the sin of Adam had for his descendants. In addition the Council declares that Adam was constituted by God in holiness and righteousness. These supernatural gifts Adam lost immediately after the infraction of the divine command. By his sinful disobedience he brought the anger of God upon his head, and consequently the death with which God had threatened him. With death came bondage under the power of him who since then has exercised the lordship of death, namely, the devil. Adam himself is thus brought to a worse condition both of soul and body. Here it is plainly pronounced that Adam was not subject to the necessity of dying, although the nature of his immortality is not further determined by the Council. In the second canon (Denz., 789) the Council speaks about the descendants of Adam and declares, quoting from Rom. v.12, that what Adam himself experienced in consequence of his sin is transmitted to his descendants. Here there is a return to the definition of Orange, which is somewhat accentuated to the extent that the influence of Adam is expressed more sharply.

The documents of the Church also emphasize that through the Fall man is affected in his freedom. According to the Council of Orange it is not permitted to hold that the sin of Adam brought about only bodily consequences for his descendants, while the freedom of the soul went unaffected. For then one would agree with the heresy of Pelagius. (Denz., 174.) Already the *Indiculus* had pronounced that it is impossible for man to rise from his sinful state by his own free will. His freedom is forever lost. But this does not mean to say that man is not responsible for his acts. We must distinguish here between impotence to achieve grace, which can be characterized as unfreedom, and the consent to sin, which goes back to the possession of free will as an aspect of human nature which cannot be lost. (Cf. Denz., 348.) Both points of view are united in the thought that the freedom of man is damaged.

The Council of Orange was directed against the semi-Pelagians, who, though to a lesser extent than the Pelagians, still failed to take the need of grace seriously enough. They thought it possible that man without grace could still think and desire something good unto salvation, and through the power of his free will arrive at the grace given by baptism. The Council declared that the free will of every human being is "vitiatum," weakened, damaged. (Denz., 181.) Here we reach the core of the matter, since the grace of Christ is at stake. The canons of Orange contain the radical confession of the impotence of man, unaided, to produce acts available to salvation, and emphasize the absolute necessity of grace.

It is clear that these definitions of the teaching authority of the Church state certain fundamental truths by which the Christian faith stands or falls. You cannot touch the dogma of original sin without robbing the redemptive work of Christ of its meaning. The saving grace of God in Christ Jesus is here at issue. When the councils concerned themselves with original sin, this grace was their central preoccupation. The gratuitousness and necessity of grace, through which God comes to the aid of sinful man, must ever be the clue in our whole discussion of the condition of man under God.

# 3

# AN ATTEMPT AT A NEW FORMULATION

From the side of the new scientific vision of human evolution great difficulties are raised concerning the usual formulation of the teaching of the Church about original sin.

First, it is difficult to accept that the human race originated in a pair of human beings which had been given the spiritual and bodily qualities traditionally attributed to Adam and Eve before the Fall. One would rather expect, in this dim beginning, types which had hardly emerged from the animal stage.

The second difficulty consists in the tension between the current formulation of the dogma of original sin, that is, in the Adam-Christ antithesis, and the ultimate possibility of polygenesis. As regards the latter, it would seem that science will never be able to give definite proof of a polygenetic origin of man. We were not there, and, on the basis of the evidence of fossils, we cannot draw a certain line between men and animals. Nevertheless, some remarks are possible. Scientific observations about the origin of species indicate that a given group does not develop from one pair of parents, but evolves as a whole in a new direction. This makes polygenesis at any rate not improbable. Against this one must put the statement of Pius XII in the encyclical *Humani Generis* that polygenism is not an open question because it is quite impossible to see how polygenism is to be reconciled with what the sources of revelation and the authoritative pronouncements of the Church have to say about original sin.

These difficulties are not slight. Yet it looks as though the modern man of science can no longer get along with the traditional presentation of the doctrine of original sin, feels unable to integrate what is given traditionally with his scientific insights. The theologian cannot ignore this. He must try to meet these difficulties. Here he can move in two directions. He can try to reduce the traditional formulations to such a form that, while preserving their essentials, they take account of the fact of evolution. And he can try to discover what elements in these formulations themselves can be laid to the account of a static image of an unevolved world.

I have spoken above of the formulation and way of presentation of the teaching about original sin. We preserve the content of revelation completely in following the latter of the two directions. Indeed, we can accept that a greater insight into the natural will operate favourably rather than prejudicially upon the insight of faith. Faith always expresses itself by the aid of concepts drawn from the empirical world. The more we know of this world, the better will the instrument be by means of which we interpret the transcendent content of faith. In this way we put the teaching about original sin against a wide background in which the doctrine of creation occupies an important place.

The biblical revelation of God as Creator is, as regards its form, strongly coloured by the primitive static image of the world. According to this static image, all things are created together in the beginning. As the world is at present, so it was created by God. When Gen. i speaks about the six days, that is a literary convention which connects with the command of Sabbath observance: "In six days the Lord made heaven and earth, and on the seventh day he rested, and was refreshed." (Exod. xxxi.17; xx.8-ii.)

To this static image are also to be traced those notions which speak about *rationes seminales,* and related ideas. If you posit, for instance, that God made unorganized matter in the beginning, but bestowed on it the power to unfold itself in ever higher forms, then it looks as though you were anticipating evolution in the creative activity of God, but in fact what you have is an additional modification of the old way of seeing things.

We read in Gen. ii.7: "Then the Lord God formed man of dust from the ground, and breathed into his nostrils the breath of life: and man became a living being." We know now that the distance between the dust and the living being, man, is a period of milliards of years. The creative act of

God, by which he created man, took milliards of years. It is one creative act, which intends the coming into being of man. *Now we must not evaluate this act of creation only with reference to the beginning but primarily with reference to the end.* The real difference between an idea of creation which functions within a static image of the world, and the idea of creation within an evolutionary image, is this, that within the static image God created *in the beginning,* and with the virtual inclusion of everything which would develop through time out of the cosmic actuality—the act of creation is completed. In the dynamic image attention is directed *to the end,* the act of creation continues. God creates the world and humanity in and unto Christ. For us who live in time this work of creation is being consummated. The intention of God's creation is consummated in the course of cosmic evolution. This point of departure governs everything in a theology of evolution.

Holy Scripture speaks several times of a creation in Christ. Its point of departure is a static image of the world, although there is at the same time a dynamic element present in the distinction between a present and a future world. God creates through the Son, and redeems and perfects through the Son. World and man, created good in the beginning, are infected by sin; hence the impossibility of man's reaching salvation without the saving hand of God. He extends this in Christ, his Son made man. In this act of salvation he has granted man a share in this divine incarnation and in the life of grace—which reaches out to the glory of the consummation, both of man and, through man, of the world.

The problem must be posed quite differently in terms of a dynamic world-image, and at the same time leads to much more insight. There is still only one gratuitousness, namely, that of the creation in Christ. The creature has no single claim, except on the basis of the fundamental gratuitousness of the creation itself, as this has been brought about by God in Christ. Completely in accord with traditional teaching, the supernatural gift of grace to man in Christ is treated purely as a gift. But this gift is now seen as the final phase of God's creative action, to which the preceding phases are directed. The situation is not that God creates man and that then, starting with this man, we discuss grace as grace.

The man whom God creates *is man as he shall be at the end*. The men who are now alive in this world are being created. They have not yet reached the stature which was the intention of God in creating. Looked at from this side the question about the gratuitousness of the supernatural order does not properly arise, because the creation of man after the image of God was something in no way due. It goes against the idea of creation to introduce the notion of what is due. Creation, as the act of a transcendent and personal God, is the taking of a sovereign and divine initiative.

The transition from the animal to the human stage is as gratuitous in its own order as that from nature to grace. No single creature can creatively raise itself to a higher mode of being; this belongs to God alone, who brings the work of creation to its conclusion. In the supernatural elevation of man there is thus an element of necessity, to the extent that the actual order of the world is a creation of communion with the glorified Christ, but there is also the element of unowed gift, to the extent that in the nature of the case creation was not a debt owed by God. If one wishes to discuss the possibility of a creation which went no further than what we call the natural order, we should have to discuss it in a world-order which does not in fact exist, and which we therefore cannot conceive.

In saying this wc have already said something about the creation of man, with the help of knowledge given us both by revelation concerning, and by scientific insight into, the coming-to-be of the world and of man. From this standpoint we can now ask on what points the static world-image influences the traditional formulation of the dogma of original sin. This question is, as I have already remarked, wholly parallel with that which an earlier generation of theologians put to Holy Scripture when the natural sciences had displaced primitive conceptions about the cosmos.

It is plain that the author of Gen. ii-iii—and this holds also for St. Paul in Rom. v—is speaking primarily about man as he knows him from experience, and even more from revelation, in his relation to God. Holy Scripture speaks to contemporaries about their relation to God, and about God in his dealings with man. This is precisely why the message of Scripture is for all men, who know themselves to share the human condition of the writers of the Bible. Even if our insight into the nature of the cosmos changes, this revelation about man stands fast.

The judgment about man expressed in the dogma of original sin is animated by the constant conviction of faith that the relation of man to his Maker is not what it should be. Man goes bowed under a deficiency which is moral as well as physical by nature. Man, as he now is, does not correspond to the intention of the Creator. What is the norm by which man's deficiency is to be measured? For the author of Gen. ii-iii this norm is the paradisal happiness of the first human pair living in the favour of God. For St. Paul this norm is primarily Christ: the salvific work of Christ has now fully revealed man's condition. The Apostle also treats the scriptural evidence from Gen. ii-iii: but he does not forget, nor must we, that the Old Testament revelation about man is completed only by confrontation with Christ.

We see that the direction in which we are looking is changing. While the author of Gen. ii-iii is looking back at what once was, St. Paul simultaneously looks forward to what shall be. But he also holds fast to a progenitor by whose willed act the original happiness was upset. This element is characteristic of the static image, through which we think of creation in the beginning: God created men, plants and animals in the forms they now have; therefore man must once have enjoyed a better condition than is his now, because the man of today is not conceivably a work of creation which corresponds to God's intention. Thus he must once have been free of the sin and the suffering which now weigh so heavily upon him.

The change in direction, brought to partial realization in St. Paul, becomes complete through the evolutionary image. While the judgment about man under God remains the same, the norm which is set in the biblical description of the first human pair loses its primacy in the measure that it has the character of a situation "in the beginning." By this I do not wish to deny that in the primitive history of man there was unfaithfulness to God's calling, of which we are still experiencing the results. I wish to say only that man must be regarded, from the first moment of his existence, as a creature going somewhere, loaded with a creaturely imperfection requiring perfection through Christ. God rested from his works after he had made man; by this expression the author of Gen. i indicates that he regards the creation of man as a completed work. The author of Gen. ii-iii also looks back to an ideal beginning. But the fact of evolution compels us to look forward to the ideal end.

Just as Gen. i is an announcement about God as Creator, in which the writer makes use of a primitive and static image of the world, so Gen. ii-iii announces the position in which man finds himself under God, and here use is made both of a static image and the connected idea of an unflawed creation in the beginning. Ours is the task today to translate the revelation so announced with the assistance of a scientific and evolutionary image. The separation of the content of revelation from that biblical form, which also affects the pronouncements of the Church, is a difficult undertaking requiring great prudence. But I wish to risk an attempt, drawing on work already published which is moving in the same direction.

Thus we posit first that we can distinguish between the content and the form of revelation. As regards the form or clothing given, it is important to notice that the method of presentation of Genesis forms a homogeneous whole, of which one cannot preserve one part while surrendering another. Thus the physical integrity of the first man is necessarily connected with the integrity of the surroundings in which he lives. It is not for nothing that the first man is placed in paradise. Therefore one cannot surrender the literal historicity of paradise and at the same time maintain the physical integrity of man. If one wishes to attribute to Adam a more perfect physical condition than that of modern man, then his surroundings must have been more perfect too. On the other hand, the condition of his spiritual life is involved with his physical condition. Thus it is evident that the first man is created in innocence; but if we regard the account of his physical prerogatives and his paradisal surroundings as unhistorical, then it follows necessarily that this innocence was the more threatened for being coupled with physical deprivations.

The question arises whether the descent of the human race from one pair must be considered to belong to the revealed content of the dogma of original sin. As we have seen, the encyclical *Humani Generis,* while it underlines the difficulty, does not categorically exclude the possibility, of reconciling the teaching about original sin with polygenesis.

The description of one pair of progenitors fits with the overall static world-image of the time. The case shows a resemblance to what happened later on to the animals: after the Flood the animals renewed their species from one pair of each kind. (Gen. vi.19-21.) In the same way the unity of the human race is concretely expressed by assuming one pair of progenitors. In the antithesis Adam-Christ which we find in St. Paul, the descent of all men from one is undoubtedly even more heavily emphasized than in Genesis. But here also there seems to be no compelling reason to regard the descent of all from one as belonging to the content of the dogma of original sin. We should find it compelling only were there no other possibility of preserving the unity and common destiny of mankind.

From a biological point of view there is no difficulty in defending the unity of mankind while keeping the door open to its polygenetic origin. Science will never be able to achieve greater certainty on the point on the basis of fossil evidence, but ultimately only by better knowledge of the development of present species. The dilemma of monogenism and polygenism is not a burning problem for science, because, in the absence of a solution, its knowledge of humankind is not undermined. Is it for theology?

We can ask ourselves whether it is theologically necessary to know anything definite about the monogenetic or polygenetic origin of man, if we can, without this knowledge, obtain adequate light about mankind under God. Do we not have sufficient if we believe that every man, by virtue of belonging to the human race, carries *in himself* the actuality of what we call original sin?

Once and for all, we know nothing concrete about the people and events of the dim prehistory of mankind. We know only that mankind, when it enters history, has the moral and religious characteristics which revelation depicts. "The whole world is accountable to God." (Rom. iii.19.) "We were by nature children of wrath, like the rest of mankind." (Eph. ii.3.) The whole world; not only the people now living, but also those who lived in the past, and those who will live in the future. They all constitute the human race, of which revelation says these and other things. If we accept this, and in this way fully honour the salvific work of Christ, do we not do enough?

The knowledge we now possess about the antiquity of man, and his biological descent from pre-human forms of life, tells us that the old ways of presenting the original sin, interpreted within a static image with temporal and spatial limitations, provide us with no real historical point of reference for our theological appreciation of the present human condition. For this we must refer to the historically accessible work of salvation done by Christ, illuminated by the prophetic teaching of both Testaments.

We have already, in passing, indicated that the salvific work of Christ is the completion of the work of creation. In

Christ, the earthly man becomes the heavenly man. (Cf. I Cor. xv.45-9.) Salvation through the Cross and the Resurrection is also a continuance of creation. The believer is freed from his sins by baptism, but at the same time he becomes a new creature already possessing, through the Spirit of Christ, the germ of a future mode of being through which he will be completed as a creature.

If we can demonstrate these two aspects in the salvific work of Christ, it is obvious that they also lie contained in the doctrine of original sin. The condition which original sin indicates implies that man as creature is unfinished, incapable of reaching his goal; and also that he finds himself in a relation to God which requires reconciliation. But there must be a connection between the one and the other, just as in the work of Christ there is a connection between the moments of creation and reconciliation. In the determination of what original sin is, it will therefore not be enough to take notice only of the moral aspect. The moral discussion of the situation which we call original sin, in its origin and persistence, goes together with the unfinishedness of the man of dust.

If, therefore, we wish to describe the condition of earthly man under God, the creaturely imperfection of man will have to be our starting-point. Here our attention naturally fastens itself on the noteworthy connection between the spiritual and physical aspects of human existence. Man is descended from the animal world, yet he possesses an immortal soul.

In the encyclical *Humani Generis* we are reminded that while we speak about the origin of man from a pre-human form of life, we must presuppose "that souls are immediately created by God." This datum seems at first sight difficult to reconcile with consistent evolutionary thought. The immediate creation of each soul looks like an irruption of God from outside the evolutionary process. But if we put it that way, we have unconsciously returned to a way of looking at things proper to the static image. We are representing evolution as the development of a situation completely established in all its constituent elements by the once-for-all action of God: there is a built-in dynamic, capable of explaining the becoming of the lower forms: if it is insufficient to produce the human spirit, there must be a brand-new, supplementary, immediate creative intervention of God.

But here, too, if we wish to hold consistently to the dynamic image, we must think from the point of view of the end. God creates towards the end; hence the coming of man from the animal is an expression of the progressive creative action of God.

We are used to explaining the effect by the cause. This may be appropriate for the phenomena which we observe, but it does not hold when we regard the evolution of the cosmos, and especially the development of life on earth. When we see how, from the unorganized matter of primal earth, man comes into being along the road of evolution, we remind ourselves of the biblical statement that God formed man out of dust and breathed life into his nostrils.

This rise is to be accounted for only by the creative action of God.

In thinking about the rise of man from an animal origin by the creative action of God, we should do well not to let ourselves be guided only by a metaphysical interpretation of the nature of the soul, but look in faith at man as the image of God. I refer back here to the natural longing for the sight of God, of which we spoke in a former chapter. This desire belongs to the essence of man. Should we deny this natural desire to man, we should deny the intellectuality of the soul, and man would no longer be man. That the human soul is not derived from the animal (in the instance of the first human beings), or from human parents, emerges from the fact that a man as person is related in his essence to God. Man is created by God as a subject who can be addressed by his Maker. This capacity to be addressed is the same as the natural desire to see the Creator who reveals himself in creation. It is the firm foundation of supernatural revelation, which would not be possible without it.

Along this way it becomes clear that the human soul is "immediately" created by God. God calls out of the actuality of the world, which is biologically prepared for it, a partner capable of a dialogue face to face. But before this is achieved, this capacity manifests itself in the natural desire to see God, which defines the essence of the man of dust, and retains its meaning under grace. By virtue of creation man possesses an inclination, suitability or disposition by means of which he is orientated to the supernatural end of seeing his Maker. To reach this consummation is impossible for man unless God meets him in grace.

This vision is a precious dynamic element in the teaching of St. Thomas, influencing his whole system. Precisely this dynamic, and the mutual relevance of nature and grace which is characteristic of this way of seeing, are enough to indicate a relationship to the evolutionary perspective. This teaching can render us great services in a theology of evolution, especially if our point of departure is the clue I have indicated—namely thinking from the consummation to which the creative activity of God is directed. We then see that the evolutionary image throws new light on the possibility of sin. Perhaps we may not expect this, considering that it is objected to Teilhard de Chardin that he does not know what to do with sin. He is said not to have reckoned fully with human freedom, and with the perversity which can reveal itself in human behaviour. But we should not forget that the sin of Adam is hard to conceive upon the basis of traditional thought. In any event, whatever image you accept, the fact of sin remains—the creature, man, comes to sin.

We must, then, start with the end phase, in which we see man in the stature willed by God, and in an unshakable adherence to God, an adherence threatened by sin. Thinking back from here, we arrive at the uncompleted men of dust which we are. The uncompleted nature of man makes the actuality of sin more conceivable than it can be in terms of a progenitor having the characteristics of the perfect man.

But further: according to the static image man appears as an unbroken being from the beginning, as a completed work on whom the Creator looked down to confirm that what he made was very good; in the dynamic representation, man stands directed to his own completion as a creature of God. On the former way of seeing it, sin appears as the collapse of a completed work; but in the light of evolution sin is revealed as the refusal of man to subject himself to God's creative will. As soon as evolution reaches the human stage and man appears, gifted with an ordination to fulfillment—an ordination which theology reduces to the natural desire for the sight of God—then the precedent creative work of God becomes a proffered gift. For the perfected man is to possess his creaturely perfection by reason of a personal decision.

Just as in the natural order the essence of man is defined by his suitability or capacity for the dialogue with God, so the essence of the perfected man is defined by open communion with God in higher freedom. It belongs to the idea of freedom that it should affirm itself. My freedom cannot be exercised by somebody else, because the originality of my own person would thereby be denied. By freedom I do not here mean freedom of choice, but freedom in respect of the good, especially freedom in respect of God, who fulfils the human essence. Freedom to choose the good or the bad is a modality of freedom in our present condition. It will fall away when the seeing of God has dawned. In the earthly phase, it is given to man to affirm his freedom by obedience to the creative will of God. Only in this way will he at the last possess himself in freedom. The creation of man in the possession of a high degree of freedom was possible, since God as transcendent Creator can posit a human freedom which is not got by striving but is given. But it is more in conformity with the creative action of God in general that he should put man in possession of a freedom which the latter has gained. In the evolutionary world-picture we see this actually happening; God's creative action is always directed to the last phase.

In the earthly phase man is open to the possibility of good and evil. In the evolutionary way of seeing things, too, sin is the collapse of man; but we describe sin more directly when we see it as the refusal of man to let the creative will of God complete itself in him. Man serves the creature instead of the Creator, and confines his longing for eternity within the closed circle of transient things.

In the totality of evolution, man is fully one whole because he is a person whom God addresses. To this creative dialogue he is beholden for the continuous unfolding of his human essence. Preserving his identity, the same man goes through two phases of evolution. In the phases of evolution which precede man death means the end: the process of life tends to its end as soon as a being has replaced itself, by generation, with another being. This is proper to man as well, looked at from the biological angle. But man is primarily a person who preserves his identity in death, and is orientated to the fulfilment which consists in unhindered communion with God.

Thus the earthly man taken as a whole is a twosided being; on the biological side he is related to the animal, and on the personal he is the image of God. This twosidedness is not a dualism, but the content of a mission to self-actualization. Merely by the fact that man is a person, his body is no longer an animal but a human body in which the spirit expresses itself. But it is not yet fully a human body; that will only happen when the spirit of man comes to full freedom in glory. Thither man cannot come except by the creative intervention of God, who calls him to himself by his self-revelation. The natural desire is certainly a capacity for the reception of the final completion, but in itself it offers no single possibility of reaching this. Only the Creator can complete man by his creative power.

If God did not show this grace, man would find himself in a situation without prospects, because it would be impossible for him to actualize himself according to the vocation buried in the innate desire to see God. But he is not abandoned to himself. He is created by God's grace for perfection. The grace of the Christian economy of salvation is in essence the continuous creative action of God. "For by *grace* you have been saved through faith; and this is not your own doing, it is the gift of God—not because of works, lest any man should boast. *For we are his workmanship, created* in Jesus Christ for good works, which God prepared beforehand, that we should walk in them." (Eph. ii.8-10.)

By regarding man as an uncompleted being we run upon

a truth which is basic for the traditional teaching about original sin: without grace man can do nothing, and the way to the sight of God is closed. For the sake of clarity let us be more precise about the agreement between the two conceptions.

Original sin in the usual sense of the term is a condition resulting from a sinful deed of the progenitor. By this sin Adam robbed human nature of grace and the gifts connected with it. Hence the state in which man is born is a state of being bereft of what God gave man in the beginning. This deprivation is, because of the sin of the progenitor, a sinful condition, even though the concept of sin here lacks the element of personal decision, and even though the notion of sin must here be thought of analogically. Had man not been created in possession of the said gifts of grace, then not possessing these gifts would imply the absence of riches which were not naturally due to him. But since he has been created so as to be actually orientated to the supernatural end, the absence of grace belongs to the sphere of sin. Original sin is a sinful bereftness of a communion with God which once was there, and should have been present now in every man. While man is in this condition, it is impossible for him to direct himself to his original destination and to live according to the moral demands which have been made of him.

The last point is found again in our description of man as an incomplete being. In himself he is in no condition to direct himself to the supernatural end and to live in accordance with the moral demands made upon him. As we shall show in the next chapter, the moral demands which God makes of man represent his divine creative will. But while in the traditional description of original sin the character of sinfulness is ascribed to this condition on account of its connection with an historical fall, we now impute sin to man's wishing to stay where he is, seeking his happiness on earth, and refusing the continuing creative action of God. Then what was at the start purely a not-yet-possessing becomes a sinful absence, because the uncompletedness, in conflict with God's will, is affirmed as a positive condition.

Up to this point we have approached original sin only on the basis of the uncompletedness of man as creature. But the condition in which man is born is not thereby determined as a sinful condition. What follows has to do with the latter aspect.

Scripture plainly teaches us that all men are guilty before God, therefore not only on the grounds of their creaturely uncompletedness, but also because their sins point to the redeeming suffering of Christ. Mankind has already made history, with the consequence that "the whole world is in the power of the evil one." (I John v.19.) Man has in fact turned against his creator and not been obedient to his creative will.

This raises the question, in what manner the individual is involved in this general condition. Is it the fact that every man makes for himself this refusal of God's grace, or is he precedently determined by an influence which affects him from mankind as a whole? And if it is the latter—which we assume—must we seek the origin of this fatal influence in the progenitor of all, or can we explain it in some other way?

We have noted, in this connection, that monogenism is not necessarily bound up with original sin, if the common destiny of man in sin, of which Holy Scripture speaks, can be maintained in some other way.

The common lot of man in sin goes together with the manner in which the human race forms a unity. This unity is affirmed by assuming a common progenitor, but it is very much a question whether relationship on the human level of evolution is really the main factor in this unity. We see that the unity of the Christian scheme of salvation, as it has already been actualized on earth, rests upon a higher principle: "There is neither Jew nor Greek, there is neither slave nor free, there is neither male nor female; for you are all one in Christ Jesus." (Gal. iii.28.) Neither race nor sex plays a part here; what is definitive is belonging to Christ. The new principle could come into operation because man was already by nature disposed to it. He is created to ask for God, and this asking God has answered through Christ in a manner which transcends all differences of race and sex. In the fact that man is by nature an asking after God there is a much higher principle of unity than can ever be constituted by descent from one progenitor. The dignity of being an image of God is given to every man by his Creator, and not by his ancestor, and the mutual communion of men resulting from this transcends by far the unit which derives from common social origins.

What has thus been positively put holds also negatively for community in sin. The condition of man, when he comes into this world, we have described as unperfected being. In this way, we drew attention to man in himself, but we have not said anything about the bonds of man with man.

Here we must return to that double character of human beings which we indicated as being a mission to self-actualization. The fulfilling of this mission does not take place simply in a dialogue of the individual with God, but in the reciprocal relation of men with each other. Our relation to our fellows is not incidental, but a necessary dimension of human existence taken as directedness to God, in the sense that the two aspects belong indissolubly together and are rooted in human being. The freedom which man must get for himself by God's grace is a freedom for service to his fellows, in which egoism is conquered and the goods of the world assumed into unselfish communion with others.

Communication with our fellows takes place through our bodiliness and its prolongation in earthly things. Here lies the region over which spirit must establish its rule, but here is the way, also, along which persons meet each other. The success of self-actualization does not depend exclusively upon the individual in his relation to God but is determined to a considerable extent by the world in which man is placed. A man born into a world of sinners already belongs, in virtue of this fact alone, to this sinful world. As I have said, we cannot take our relation to our fellows as something incidental and external. This relation belongs to human nature. The world in which man stands is the necessary complement of his individual existence.

That is precisely why the condition of the world is codeterminate for the condition of the man born into the world. If the world as a whole lies in the power of the Evil One, this power extends to the child when he is born, not in the form of personal guilt, but as a datum which is codeterminative for his relationship with God. The fact that man cannot actualize his natural desire for the sight of God without the gracious mediation of the Creator now implies difficulty because of the co-determining influence of the sinful world. The body is already a territory to be gained by struggle, but when we add the negative influence of the sinful human community, then the lordship of the spirit becomes impossible unless God in his mercy takes away the sin of the world and founds a community in salvation in which perspective on the future life once more opens.

The traditional conception of original sin accompanies a way of thinking in which the significance of the relationship is underestimated and attention is directed almost exclusively to what can be referred to the individual subject. One speaks about the original sin of the individual person and describes this condition as inherent in the man born of Adam. But man is totally the subject of relations; to God, in the first place, and also to his fellows. By this his own personality and his personal characteristics are not denied; I wish only to say that his personal characteristics are not thinkable outside these relations. Neither is original sin thinkable outside the framework of actual relations. Actual personal relations with our fellows are therefore much more constitutive of what a man is than is common descent from one progenitor. For the mutual relationship of persons living now it makes no difference whether they are descended from one ancestor or from many, and the relation of all to this progenitor or these progenitors can hardly be called a personal relationship. If we bring original sin into connection with man in a sinful world, we do no injustice to this state of affairs. Our description of original sin includes the two components which St. Paul mentions in Eph. ii.1-3, before he describes mankind as "children of wrath." He mentions the influence of "this world," and the "spirit which is now at work among the sons of disobedience," but next to these he also mentions the desires of the flesh. The desires of the flesh are complied with, but we cannot isolate this fact from the influence on man exercised from without by the world which lies in the power of the Evil One.

If, after this explanation, we are to define original sin, it would have to be as follows: Original sin is the powerlessness, arising from nature, of man in his uncompletedness as creature to reach his freedom and to realize the desire to see God, *insofar as* this impotence is put into the context of a sinful world.

In conclusion we can also ask ourselves how the whole of mankind can be ruled by sin, while the first man or men were created in innocence. The history of prehistoric man inhabiting this earth thousands of centuries ago is a closed book to us; but in connection with what has been said about the influence which the community asserts over the individual, it is possible to see mankind in its totality as the cause of the present state of affairs. Sin has taken root in the human community, in order to rule it as a tyrannizing power. Whoever is born into this community is irrevocably delivered to this power.

Baptism places man in the Church as the new community of salvation, the Body of Christ. Baptism is a new creation, and at the same time a liberation from the power of sin. As new creation baptism places man in the ambit of life of the heavenly Man, who, through his work of salvation, has conquered sin.

Birth from Christian parents in the Church of Christ is already in itself of significance for the newly born child, because then the influence of the sinful world is already turned aside by a protective milieu. Just as for the adult justification is preceded by preparatory acts, so the Christian family is, for the newly born child, a comparable preparation for its assumption into the Body of Christ.

In the course of our exposition it has already appeared that Christian grace has the character of a creative activity. Insofar as man by sin has dimmed his lustre and broken himself down as creature, grace is also healing. This conception of grace and of the self-revelation of God is not to be understood as though we had to do with a physical event, a sort of natural process, by which sin, as revolt against God, and the forgiveness of sin by the death of Christ on the cross, are not to be judged according to their own proper depth and seriousness. In the following chapter I shall show what happens on the level of personal encounter in the revelation of God, as the creative action of God. The moral demands which God makes represent his creative will. His personal revelation stands in the centre of his creative activity. Grace perfects nature.

# 4

# CREATIVE REVELATION

Modern studies in biblical anthropology indicate that the sacred writers accented the unity of human nature more heavily than we are accustomed to do. This way of seeing the unity of man is founded, more or less as in modern philosophic phenomenology, in a view of man which does not set out from a statically given "man" but sees man as subjectivity appearing in bodiliness. My fellow human, who meets me, I see as a bodily being, and in this bodily mode of appearance the prerogatives which characterize a person are revealed. The concept of person is unknown in the Bible, but what we understand philosophically by a person is by no means unknown. According to the Bible, personal existence is rooted in the heart. When we read in Prov. iv.23 that the origin of life is in the heart, we are to understand that life, in the biblical sense, is the happy and in all ways successful life which is pleasing to Yahweh, built up out of the heart, which is the source of the aims and thoughts which direct man. That is why, again according to

Prov. iv.23, the heart must be guarded with the utmost care, because it can also be the point of departure for the destruction of man.

I do not seek in any way to support my position from the fact that biblical thinking shows a certain relationship to modern existential phenomenology. We are concerned only with the consistent affirmation of man as a subjectivity turned to God as we find this in the Bible. Thus our exegesis will have to contain its own credentials.

To say that man is a unity is to say that he is the subject of his human acts as an undivided totality. A man acts as embodied subjectivity when he eats and drinks, but just as much when he desires, hopes, or loves, and especially when he responds to the revelation of God. There is no territory of human action where the soul alone is active.

This has an important consequence which is at the same time one of the foundations of our whole demonstration, that moral action belongs to the man, not to the soul alone. The Old Testament conception of the moral order connects closely with this. If, on the basis of an anthropological dualism, we regard the soul rather than the person as the subject of ethical actions, without making due allowance for the unity of man, then, in the cosmic actuality, we mark off a special area for the relation of the human soul to God. The moral order is thus confined to this area, and in a sense stands loose from the material cosmic order, to which man belongs with his body.

A main feature of the Old Testament way of looking at

man and the world as this developed, especially after the Exile, within the framework of the belief in a transcendent God is the interweaving of the moral order with the whole of the order of creation. All of this is thought about in terms of a static image. I quote here two texts from the Psalms, in which the static character of the world-order is affirmed with emphasis:

> For ever, O Lord, thy word
> is firmly fixed in the heavens.
> Thy faithfulness endures to all generations;
> thou hast established the earth and it stands
> fast.
> By thy appointment they stand this day;
> for all things are thy servants.
>
> [Ps. cxix.89-91]

The word of Yahweh, about which *v.* 89 speaks, is everywhere in the rest of the psalm the command of Yahweh to man. But here it is his creative command that stands fast in the heavens. Heaven together with earth (*v.* 90) constitutes the universe (*v.* 91). The creative word of Yahweh stands fast in heaven because it guarantees the stability of heaven. So also does the faithfulness of Yahweh guarantee the stability of the earth. As servants of Yahweh, heaven and earth stand ready to carry out his commands.

> Praise him, sun and moon,
> praise him, all you shining stars!

Praise him, you highest heavens,
and you waters above the heavens!
Let them praise the name of the Lord!
For he commanded and they were created,
and he established them for ever and ever;
he fixed their bounds which cannot be passed.

[Ps. cxlviii.3-6]

Especially in the last verse the static character of the universe comes strongly to the fore. The stability of the universe was for the Israelites a convincing proof of God's unshakable faithfulness towards his creation, therefore towards his people also: "If you can break my covenant with the day and my covenant with the night, so that day and night will not come at their appointed time, then also my covenant with David my servant may be broken!" (Jer. xxxiii.20.) But we are not to forget here that the immovable fidelity of Yahweh to his people will be realized in *history*. Here everything becomes dynamic, but behind this dynamic stands God's unalterable will to salvation, expressing itself in the stability of the universe. Thus does God's eternal faithfulness to the Covenant utter itself; as in the stability of the universe, so in the history of the people.

In the verses quoted from the Psalms, we notice that the attitude of the universe in respect to Yahweh is one of service; the universe carries out the command of Yahweh. The hymn to the divine Wisdom, which we come upon in Baruch iii and iv, gives a fine expression to this thought:

He who sends forth the light, and it goes,
called it, and it obeyed him in fear;
the stars shone in their watches and were glad;
he called them, and they said, "Here we are!"
They shone with gladness for him who made
them.

[Baruch iii.33-5]

When we search in the Old Testament for the place of this view within the whole of the theology of the time, we arrive properly at the moral order whose norm is the Law. We have already remarked in connection with Ps. cxix.89 that the expression "word of Yahweh" is used everywhere else in the psalm for God's command to man. Only in *v.* 89 does the expression refer to the creative word. The "word of Yahweh" unites in itself both the creative and the moral command:

He sends forth his command to the earth;
his word runs swiftly.
He gives snow like wool;
he scatters hoarfrost like ashes.

He casts forth his ice like morsels;
who can stand before his cold?

He sends forth his word, and melts them;
he makes his wind blow, and the waters flow.
He declares his word to Jacob,

his statutes and ordinances to Israel.
He has not dealt thus with any other nation;
they do not know his ordinances.

[Ps. cxlvii.15-20]

The background of the habit of regarding the word of Yahweh both as creative word and as moral command is the conviction *that the moral command, too, is creative.* Yahweh directs his creative word to the chaos to order it and to fill it with all sorts of creatures. (Gen. i.) Ever since, the universe exists in constant obedience to God's creative will. Natural phenomena occur according to fixed laws. The whole of creation is saturated with built-in lawfulness. Thus the whole universe in all its facets shows forth a harmony which is to be explained only by the immeasurable wisdom of the Creator which displays its workings here.

When he gave to the wind its weight,
and meted out the waters by measure;
when he made a decree for the rain,
and a way for the lightning of the thunder.

[Job xxviii.25-6]

Just as everything exists in harmony, and moves and lives in obedience to God's sovereign creative will, so, too, man lives in his peculiar position in the visible universe, thanks to his obedience to God's commands. What follows on the passage in Ps. cxix. 89-91, which I quoted above, makes this appear clearly:

If thy law had not been my delight,
I should have perished in my affliction.
I will never forget thy precepts;
for by them thou hast given me life.

[Ps. cxix.92-3]

God's will is creative also when he expresses himself in the moral law. The fact that the moral law is directed to a man who, as engaged in a personal dialogue with God, has the possibility of obeying or not obeying God's law diminishes nothing of the creative character of the moral law. When man obeys, God realizes his creative will in him, resulting in the gift of *life*. The Old Testament theological conception of "life" is the completed human existence under the love of the Creator. Man experiences life inwardly as joy and peace, which knows itself to be guaranteed by the pleasure of Yahweh. The creative wisdom of God, which in Prov. viii addresses itself warningly to man, commends itself in the words:

For he who finds me finds life
and obtains favours from the Lord;
but he who misses me injures himself;
all who hate me love death.

[Prov. viii.35]

In its outward-going aspects, life is characterized by communion and the respect of one's fellows, a numerous progeny and disposition over the goods of this world.

"Length of days" is also added, reaching a ripe old age. In the Wisdom literature the aspects of a happy life are occasionally summed up. (Ecclus. i.14-21; Prov. iii.13-26; Ps. cxii etc.)

But when man refuses God's commands he enters the realm of *death*. Here the theological conception of death enters which, together with the conception of life, is of the highest importance for understanding the New Testament announcement of salvation. The concepts of life and death can be penetrated only in relation to the acceptance or refusal of God's moral law, which is, in the strict sense of the term, a creative command.

The whole of this theological insight corresponds with the conception of man as the *bodily subject* of the meeting with God. Man faces God in an existence which is wholly interwoven with that of the world. This life, which is the consequence of obedience, is thus the earthly life in all its dimensions. Death, on the other hand, is marked by the snapping of the link with God and with the world of the living. The poet of Ps. lxxxviii expresses the experience of this torn existence in a striking way.

To complete the preceding ideas we must add two further remarks.

In the first place, one can rightly object against the parallelism between the creative command which is addressed to the non-human world, and the moral command addressed to man, that, in the first instance, the command of God relates to the existence of the creature as such, whereas the moral command already presupposes the partner in the dialogue. The Israelites would have seen this, and yet they never press the distinction. For the distinction lies contained in the fact that life and death are seen as qualifications of our existence. They must not be put on the same level as being and non-being in the metaphysical sense of the words. But it remains valid to say that life and death qualify human existence in its *totality*. There is nothing in man which stands outside these conditions. There is thus in the creature a general substrate, which we can call existence, and a qualification which we can designate by life or death. This qualification is immediately connected with the relationship to God, and it is solely in the light of this qualification that the Hebrew saw creation.

Because of the exceptional importance of this judgment, on which we shall continually have to rely, I give here additional concrete illustration. "Then the Lord God formed man of dust from the ground, and breathed into his nostrils the breath of life; and man became a living being." (Gen. ii.7.) We might think that we were talking here about the creation of man unqualified by the relation with God, but then we should miss the essential. In the creative lifegiving breath of God there resides not only the power to call man into existence, but also and especially to make him a being directed to God. Out of the dust of the earth God evokes a partner in a dialogue. Another example: "In him [the Word] was life, and the life was the light of men." (John i.4.) The "light of men" refers to man's reason, his intelligence. But the intelligence is light only when directed to God. Otherwise it is darkness. We have to do here not with intelligence as such, nor with the supernatural light of grace, but with the intelligence as directed to God. Later we shall deal with these examples at length.

The second remark concerns the classical teaching about individual rewards and punishment in the Sapiential books. According to this literature the godly on earth are rewarded with life; the sinner, for his sins, is punished with death. This is a direct consequence of the insight that the commands of God are creative. Life and death are connected by an inner necessity with the attitude which man takes up to God's commands. At that time people did not have the way out provided by rewards after death.

For centuries ancient Israel worded its theological insights concerning life and death by the aid of an ancient image according to which the surface of the earth was the land of the living, and the subterranean *sheol* the abode of the dead, indicated by the name *rephaim,* "the shades." Here the bond with Jahweh is broken: "The dead do not praise Jahweh." (Ps. cxv.17.) A happy continued existence of the godly after death is unknown. "Length of days" is the most that men can achieve. Hence the concentration upon life and death as reward and punishment within the space of earthly existence. This produces special difficulty in respect of death, seeing that earthly rewards and punishments are difficult to connect with dying. Punishment for sin is thus seen as an early, above all violent, death. This is accompanied by the possibility of regarding the worldly misfortune of illness as an outpost of death. The underworld is represented as a power which stretches its greedy arms towards the dwellers on earth. In this way men on earth could already be touched by the realm of death.

This doctrine of retribution frequently did not square with the facts, and became a pressing problem. The Book of Job witnesses to this. The prophet Jeremiah presents God with the problem of equity: "Why does the way of the wicked prosper? Why do all who are treacherous thrive?" (Jer. xii.1.) It is not clear when and where this scheme of rewards is broken through. Probably it occurred earlier than the texts would suggest. In any event the Book of Wisdom, written shortly before our era and in the milieu of an Alexandrian *diaspora,* gives striking evidence of this breakthrough. While the poet of Ps. lxxxviii says that the dead are out of the reach of God, we read here that the souls of the just who have been martyred by the enemies of God are in the hands of God and have found peace. (Wisd. of Sol. iii.1-4.)

How do the unity of man and the integration of the moral order into the order of creation look in this new perspective? In the old doctrine of rewards there appeared to be a connection between the conception of man as indivisible bodily subject and the interweaving of the moral with the created order. Here everything relates. The creative activity of God coincides with his word of command. There is no distinction between the action of God as Creator and of God as Legislator. Man, together with the world in which he stands, listens to the divine command.

This connection is sustained in the new eschatological view. It is true that hard theological work, in the light of revelation, will have to be done before the balance is again restored. The Book of Wisdom recognizes a future for man on the other side of death, but it speaks less clearly about the eschatology of the cosmos. St. Paul provides the necessary balance when he states that creation will share in the glory of the children of God. (Rom. viii.19-23.) In the final eschatological view of Scripture there is mention of a future world in which righteousness dwells (2 Pet. iii.13), while the form of the present world is seen as passing away. (1 Cor. vi.31.) God renews everything. (Rev. xxi.1-5.)

With all this, we must realize clearly that the old doctrine of rewards contains imperishable elements. The view of man as embodied subjectivity, and the interweaving of the moral order with the creative order, formed in their mutual connection the main content of this doctrine of rewards. What it lacked was a grasp of the full dimension of man. Only when Old Testament piety began to comprehend that God faithfully preserved man even after death did it come to realize that this destiny to eternity could not be actualized in a terrestrial body. It sees then that life and death are more deeply rooted in man than can be realized in a mode of being which is confined to an earthly existence. But the core of the old view is carried forward when the perspective widens onto a reward beyond the grave. "If the dead are not raised, let us eat and drink, for tomorrow we die." (1 Cor. xv.32.) All or nothing. But always the realities of life and death are regarded as qualifications of man as the creature of God, under the sign of the attitude which man takes to his Maker. Resurrection unto life is for the righteous only, and the sinner is already dead on earth.

This short sketch of the doctrine of rewards has to stand in order to serve as the background for the demonstration that the self-revelation of God in Holy Scripture has a creative character. The revelation of God fulfils itself in many ways, but we are here concerned with revelation in the most real sense, which consists in the presence of God to the depths of man. From the side of man, this revelation is completed in *knowing* God, and from the side of God, in his giving himself to be known. This knowing can be built up only in the accord of the human being with the will of God in the execution of his commands. "For wisdom will come into your heart, and knowledge will be pleasant to your soul." (Prov. ii.10.) Wisdom is equated here with "the fear of Yahweh" which is realized in the observance of his commands. By this route wisdom becomes the intimate experience of the presence of God. The description of the New Covenant formulated by Jeremiah (xxxi.31-4) and repeated in the Letter to the Hebrews (viii.8-12) contains as prelude the statement that God in the coming time of salvation will write his law on the hearts of men. The prophet intends to say that God will inspire man to the fulfilment of his will. By this means the obedient will become the People of God, and all men will *know* Yahweh personally. The connection between obedience to God's will and knowing God finds utterance as well in the words of Jesus: "He who has my commandments and keeps them, he it is who loves me; and he who loves me will be loved by my Father, and I will love him and *manifest* myself to him." (John xiv.21.)

It is well known that the biblical conception of *knowing* is much higher in content than ours. In the biblical conception knowledge rises from the heart. It surprises us moderns that the Orientals took so little interest in the function of the brain. Does this derive from ignorance of anatomy? We should seek for an explanation rather in the fact that conceptual consideration not orientated to action was unthinkable. What was of concern was the purposiveness of the intelligence, and the springs of this are in the heart. Thoughts arise in the heart. Perhaps we still have something to learn from this.

In the Bible, knowledge, just because of its directedness to the Creator, is immediately connected with the existence of man as the creature of God. That is why the knowledge of God, on the basis of his self-revelation, is, in the full sense of the words, nothing other than *created becoming*. "You have put on the *new nature,* which is being renewed in *knowledge* after the image of its *creator*." (Col. iii.10.) We find the same thought in a slightly varied form in Eph. iv.24: "[You must] be renewed in the spirit of your minds [in your mentality], and put on the new nature, created after the likeness of God in true righteousness and holiness." Another example: "And this is eternal *life,* that they *know* thee, the only true God, and Jesus Christ whom thou hast sent." (John xvii.3.) We are not to turn this knowing of God into a thin conceptual relationship but must comprehend it as the fulfilment of man as creature.

We see that the moral command set by God which, in the history of revelation, started off originally as a code, is already in the Old Testament to take the form of a divine inspiration in the heart of man. In Ps. cxix the poet turns to God, praying to know his law. The writer does not ask for a theoretical knowledge, which he certainly did not lack. He is asking for an internal seeing of the will of God in the concrete situations of life. "I will run in the way of thy commandments when thou enlargest my understanding. Thy word is a lamp to my feet and a light to my path. Thy testimonies are my heritage forever; yea, they are the joy of my heart. The unfolding of thy words gives light; it imparts understanding to the simple. Make thy face shine upon thy servant, and teach me thy statutes." (*vv.* 32, 105, 111, 130, 135.) In this manner the knowledge of the law becomes the creative presence of God, comparable with God's presence in the world. "The earth, O Lord, is full of thy steadfast love; teach me thy statutes!" (*v.* 64.) This divine instruction in the law is the perfecting of God's creative work in man. "Thy hands have made and fashioned me; give me understanding, that I may learn thy commandments." (*v.* 73.)

In this way the knowledge of the law of God becomes the knowledge of God, the Creator. On the side of man this knowledge is the same as being created. From the side of God the moral demand becomes an inspiring of the human heart, and God himself is present to man. His word, which first appears as a command which compels from without, interiorizes itself to the Word which is God, and lives in the heart as the light of men.

In this book we are trying to formulate the revelation of sin and salvation using the evolutionary image. Hence these considerations are of essential concern for our purpose. Were the self-revelation of God to man, of which Scripture speaks, not in the strictest sense a creative revelation, we could say nothing further by the aid of the evolutionary image of the world, since this conception of the world implies a progressive creative action of God directed to a final consummation. Were God in his supernatural revelation no longer the creator God, and did he act in some other manner than creatively, then evolution would come to its end here in a meaningless way. We could do nothing towards describing God's work of salvation through Christ by using the contemporary dynamic image.

If we see the self-revelation of God as the progressive creative action of God, then this view not only squares well with the fact of evolution but at the same time illuminates the manner in which, from a theological standpoint, evolution completes itself. Evolution, as we said in Chapter 3, must not be conceived as if God in the beginning had given his creation the power to unfold itself in ever higher forms, but rather as if evolution is itself the humanly apprehensible side of the progressively creative action of God. The essential point of our endeavour gains clarity from the traditional teaching of the Church on grace. We have already referred to this teaching when we said that the natural desire of man to see God was a disposition to the reception of final completion, but did not in itself present any possibility of reaching this completion. Only the Creator can complete man by his creative grace. The doctrine of Christian grace indicates how evolution completes itself on the human level. Here we see with full clarity that there is in man a disposition to receive a completion, but at the same time it is apparent that this disposition does not have the character of an inbuilt dynamic power which has merely to unfold itself in order to bring man to the sight of God. If we ascribed to man the possibility of reaching his end by his own powers, we should go contrary to the core of the Christian faith.

The mystery of Christian grace consists in an approach of God to man, to which man, as created becoming, responds. This relationship completes itself through dialogue. God speaks to man and man answers. The answer of man is a being-human in a new way, which is a gift of God the Creator. Thus we see that on the one hand Christian grace, as a favour of God, is a creative action of God, the Sovereign. It is totally a gift, just because grace originates in the Creator. But on the other hand grace is entirely of man, because it is he who is created. In this way we can gain some insight into the statement that the faith and works of the justified are wholly gifts of God, while they are nevertheless human activities through and through. They come completely from the Creator, and completely from man.

Analogically and by extension, we can say the same about creation on the lower levels. Here, too, the development to higher modes of being and of life flows wholly from the creatures. This is what science perceives when it establishes the fact of evolution, or studies the dynamics of development. Yet from the viewpoint of the theology of creation we must say that this development at the same time manifests the progressive action of God, and that the creation has not the built-in power to evolve independently to higher forms. In this way, and from our knowledge of creation on the human level, light is thrown on the dynamics of all evolution.

The creation of terrestrial man is being completed. Man is on the way to a mysterious future, ever invited and guided by the self-revelation of God, until he shall see the Creator unveiled. In this seeing, man does not become God. He remains totally a creature, though having a decisively higher mode of being than he now possesses. The creaturely actuality of present man will be recovered analogically in the man to come. Man now and man to come represent two modes of creaturely being related analogically to each other. This becomes clear as soon as we realize that God's revelation is creative. The knowledge which we now have of God's revealing of himself is an analogue of the knowledge which we shall have of God in the future. That is why the human creature, as he is at present, is an analogue of the human creature to be. This analogy is somewhat like that which exists between the animal and man in his present state.

Creation does not stop somewhere in its progress, to make room for a kind which transcends what can be created. Creation is summoned to be transformed into glory from within. It remains creation through and through, but at the future higher level, glorified man is to respond to the vision of God.

# 5

# CREATION BY WISDOM

In the preceding chapter I have already briefly proposed that the sanctifying work of Christ operates not merely within the whole of the human race, but within the whole universe. But if it be true that in the sanctifying work of Christ there lies the point of departure for a new creation of the world, it follows that the antithesis Adam-Christ has only a contracted character, insofar as it refers only to the human race. Beyond this lies the cosmic dimension of salvation, which finds its polar opposite, or rather, its preparation, in the creation of the universe in Christ.

The New Testament expressly connects the first and the second creations. We have already briefly indicated the main relevant texts. They are Heb. i-ii and Col. i.15-20.

Before describing the creation in Christ we must first say something about what is, in my opinion, an erroneous view to be found nowadays in biblical theology. The biblical notion of creation in Christ is interpreted as though Christ were present at creation as the Son of God made man. His humanity is supposed in some mysterious way to have played a role in the origin of the world, as well as being an operative mediating cause. One of the texts on which this interpretation rests is, precisely, Col. i.15-17. In the verses preceding this passage the Apostle is talking about salvation through Christ. The same Christ, apparently therefore the Son made man, is the subject of the sentence which commences in *v.* 15, and which speaks about the creation of all things in him.

But this exegesis rests on a misunderstanding arising from the application of scholastic concepts to the biblical message. When scholastic theology speaks about Christ, it assumes that it is always speaking about the Son of God made man. But the position is different in Holy Scripture and in the works of the Fathers. They see in Christ the eternal Word of the Father appearing. And because the Word appears in Christ, identical in person, and because the eternal Word is accessible to us only in Christ, people speak about Christ as though they had to do with his pre-existence. The defenders of the opinion mentioned have not realized that they would then have to say that the humanity of Christ is consubstantial with the Father: we always confess in the Creed that our Lord Jesus Christ is born of the Father before all worlds.

Here we immediately have a good point of departure for our exposition. Whom do the sacred writers see making an appearance when they say that everything is created in Christ? The terminology of Col. i.15 and Heb. i.3 points distinctly in the direction of the Sapiential literature, and especially to Wisd. of Sol. vii.25-6. Here it is said of the divine Wisdom that it is "a pure emanation of the glory of the Almighty" and "a reflection of eternal light." Further, we read in Wisd. of Sol. vii.26 that Wisdom is an image of God's goodness, an expression which we can compare with Col. i.15: "He is the image of the invisible God." These parallels permit us to assume that Christ is here seen as the revelation of the divine wisdom, about which the Wisdom books speak.

The Wisdom books provide us with the possibility of achieving greater clarity about the idea that everything is created in Christ. There we read, in various passages, that God creates through his wisdom. It now becomes relevant to investigate what the characteristics of this divine wisdom were which were involved in the creation of the world.

When the Jew calls God wise, he takes his stand on the conception of wisdom which he finds in his everyday language. There wisdom is the practical wisdom of life which is able to arrive at a good result by the use of the right means. Applied to human life itself, wisdom is directive for the construction of human existence according to the will of God. The typical function of the wise man is to give counsel. God possesses wisdom analogously. That is why he needs no counsellor (Isa. xl.13-14 etc.)—a thought which still echoes in Rom. xi.34.

Of much more importance is the concept of *power* which, throughout, is combined with wisdom. Perhaps we can explain the combination by saying that people entertained the idea that the wise man knew how to carry out his purposes. Human wisdom also goes together with power. (Isa. x.13; Jer. ix.22.) However that may be, when St. Paul in 1 Cor. i.24 calls Christ the power and the wisdom of God, he is referring to an old and well-established parallelism. Here are a few texts, which leave out of account the books of Ecclesiasticus and Wisdom:

He determines the number of the stars,
he gives to all of them their names.
Great is our Lord and abundant in power;
his understanding is beyond measure.

[Ps. cxlvii.4-5]

He is wise in heart and mighty in strength.
By his power he stilled the sea;
by his understanding he smote Rahab.

[Job. ix.4]

It is he who made the earth by his power,
who established the world by his wisdom,
and by his understanding stretched out the
heavens.

[Jer. x.12]

The Lord is the everlasting God,
the Creator of the ends of the earth.
He does not faint or grow weary,
his understanding is unsearchable.

[Isa. xl.28]

. . . to whom belong wisdom and might.

[Dan. ii.20]

According to Prov. viii.14 the divine wisdom has for man counsel and sound wisdom, insight and strength. This reminds us of the description of the spirit which, according to Isa. xi.2, will rest on the Messiah: ". . . the spirit of wisdom and understanding, the spirit of counsel and might, the spirit of knowledge and the fear of the Lord." This typical collocation of wisdom and strength is explicable only if wisdom, too, is regarded as the creative power of God, and therefore as the omnipotence of the Creator working outwardly. The Greek translator of Job xi.46a actually uses the expression "the power of the wisdom." We find the same mode of expression in Ecclus. xlii.21: "He has ordained the splendours of his wisdom,"[1] by which the writer intends to say that God by his wisdom produces the creatures according to their measure and weight. In Isa. xl.13 the same thing is said about the spirit of Yahweh, while in the preceding verse the measures and weights of created things are mentioned.

The combination of wisdom and power, however, comes most strongly to the fore in Wisd. of Sol. vii.22-viii. I shall not analyse the whole passage here, but shall only indicate the following circumscriptions of the divine wisdom: "She is a pure emanation of the glory of the Almighty . . . a spotless mirror of the working of God." (*vv.* 25, 26.) "Though she is but one she can do all things, and while

[1] Knox, "How great the wisdom that so ordered all things."

remaining in herself, she renews all things . . . She reaches mightily from one end of the earth to the other and she orders all things well." (vii.27; viii.1.)

Although this book accepts an old tradition, the terminology also points in the direction of the Stoa. We shall not pursue this further, but wish to remark in passing that this book does not, any more than did the Stoic philosophers, arrive at the metaphysical concept of the immaterial. The divine Wisdom is represented as being the very finest and purest matter, and "penetrating through all spirits that are intelligent and pure and most subtle." (vii.23.) This fineness and purity enables her to be everywhere present with her creative power: "Because of her pureness she pervades and penetrates all things." (vii.24.)

This material presentation of God ought not to shock us. If one is used to thinking concretely, one represents spirit by refining the material infinitely. We think in metaphysical abstractions, so that in the concept of the immaterial we retain only what is negative.

But we have deviated somewhat from our subject. We saw that Wisdom is apprehended as a divine *power*. Another aspect of Wisdom is her *multiplicity*. This property has a connection with the multiplicity of creatures in their endless variety and in their precisely established measures and weights. Wisd. of Sol. xi.20 unites these in one sentence: "Thou hast arranged all things by measure and number and weight." Such a work of creation can be carried through only by means of a truly divine wisdom, in which everything is included as in its source. The thoughts of God are more numerous than the sands of the sea. (Ps. cxxxix.17-18.) The wonders which God has done cannot be counted. (Ps. xl.6.)

Job 28 is of singular interest. In a hymn of praise to Wisdom, the poet asks who has ever fathomed her. The answer is that God alone knows the path that leads to Wisdom. He alone knows where she dwells:

> For he looks to the ends of the earth,
> and sees everything under the heavens.
> When he gave to the wind its weight,
> and meted out the waters by measure;
> when he made a decree for the rain,
> and a way for the lightning of the thunder;
> then he saw it and declared it;
> he established it and searched it out.[2]
>
> [*vv.* 24-7]

God alone has measured Wisdom; to men his works remain unfathomable and unaccountable. (Job v.9.) Nobody other than God can count the clouds by his wisdom. (Job xxxviii.37.) The matter is plain: God's wisdom contains an infinity of creative thoughts which are realized in the visible creation. Ecclus. i.9 repeats Job xxviii.27: He saw Wisdom and numbered her. Wisd. of Sol. vii.23 formulates in two words both the unity and the multiplicity of Wisdom: of her

[2] Knox, "traced its plan, and set all in order, and mastered it." (*v.* 27.)

nature she is one (*monogenes*), and at the same time multiple (*polumeres*); a thought that recurs in *v.* 27: though she is one, she can do all things.

From the above one can already gain an impression of the concrete image of the divine Wisdom formed by the theologians of Israel. On the one hand, Wisdom is God's creative power: on the other (and more directly in line with the common conception of wisdom) the source of the order of the universe.

This order we have already verified in the measures and weights which are set for creatures. She is also and especially present in the lawfulness with which the phenomena of nature move to their end. In a previous chapter we became acquainted with the Jewish conception of the interlacing union of the moral order and the physical order of creation. Here this again becomes relevant. Now we come at last to that function of Wisdom which has the preeminence in the Wisdom books. Wisdom is the source of all the laws which rule the cosmic happenings, and especially of the moral law which is given to Israel.

Laws are given to creatures. We have just seen that in Job xxviii.26: " . . . when he made a decree for the rain." Sometimes we hear also that creatures may not infringe the laws given by God, the same verb being used as is applied to ordinary human infringements of the Law. (Prov. viii.29; Jer. v.22.) But the main interest is in the law which is prescribed for man. The hymn to the divine Wisdom in the Sapiential literature displays three successive ideas, which are clearly discernible in, for instance, Prov. viii. First, Wisdom pre-exists, is older than the world, though connected with the creation of the world. (*vv.* 22-6.) Second, she mediates in the creation of the world, and in the confirmation of its laws. (*vv.* 27-9.) Thirdly, she comes down to men to instruct them in God's will, so that they may find life. (*vv.* 30-6.) We can trace this structure in Ecclus. xxiv, and, without mention of the origin of Wisdom in God, in Wisd. of Sol. vii.22-9; and Baruch iii.29-38. It is not difficult to uncover the same plan in John i.1-5.

Thus Wisdom has a creative function, which contains the instruction of man in the will of God, an activity directed to the completion of man as creature. Wisdom, by her interior inspiration, is actively present in man. Rather than cite a number of texts which will bring to light the active ingression of Wisdom into human life, I shall be satisfied to cite some verses of the prayer which the author of Wisdom puts in the mouth of Solomon (ix.9-10; 13-18):

> With thee is wisdom, who knows thy works
> and was present when thou didst make the
>   world,
> and who understands what is pleasing in thy
>   sight
> and what is right according to thy command-
>   ments.
> Send her forth from the holy heavens,
> and from the throne of thy glory send her,

that she may be with me and toil,
and that I may learn what is pleasing to thee.

For what man can learn the counsel of God?
Or who can discern what the Lord wills?
For the reasoning of mortals is worthless,
and our designs are likely to fall,
for a perishable body weighs down the soul,
and his earthly tent burdens the thoughtful
  mind.
We can hardly guess at what is on earth,
and what is at hand we find with labour;
but who has traced out what is in the heavens?
Who has learned thy counsel, unless thou hast
  given wisdom
and sent thy holy Spirit from on high?
And thus the paths of those on earth were set
  right,
and men were taught what pleases thee,
and were saved by wisdom.

In all this we have concretely presented to our eyes what the writers of the New Testament saw in Christ when they called him by the names by which the godly of earlier days had designated Wisdom. Wisdom is everywhere present in the universe, as the ordering and teaching creative power of God. St. Paul calls Christ "the first-born of all creation" (Col. i.15), by which he proposes that Christ, the wisdom of God, comes forth from God together with the whole of creation. The New Testament is not concerned with the pre-existence of the Son, except insofar as this pre-existence can throw light on the person of Christ, and on the creative and redemptive work which is done by him. (John i.1-3; Col. i.17; Heb. i.3; Phil. ii.6-11.) In the formula "the first-born of all creation" (Col. i.15 cf. Rev. iii.14, "the beginning of God's creation") two ideas are united in one: the Son belongs to creation, of which he is the First-born, but as First-born he transcends creation. The title of First-born also expresses that he is before all worlds. (*v.* 17.)

In passing we may mention, too, the passage in John i.15, to show the resemblance of these verses to the hymn to Wisdom in the Old Testament. They present a good point of departure for going more closely into the relation of Wisdom or the Word to the light which is in men.

In the beginning was the Word,
and the Word was with God,
and the Word was God.
He was in the beginning with God;
all things were made through him,
and without him was not anything made that
  was made.
In him was life,
and the life was the light of men.
The light shines in the darkness,
and the darkness has not overcome it.

We are especially concerned with the last lines. In him was life. Here "life" is not so much a static attribute of the Word as the divine life seen as the salvation of men. Through the Logos God communicates his life to man. This idea occurs elsewhere in the Gospel. "As the living Father sent me, and I live because of the Father, so he who eats me will live because of me." (vi.57.) Jesus is here speaking, as the Son made man, about the sacramental communication of life. But in i.4 the Word is considered in his pre-existence. We are in the sphere of the hymn to Wisdom: after all things have come into being through the Word (Wisdom), the Word comes especially to men to give them life through interior light.

What is the "light of men"? Before answering this question, we must first take our stand on the position that we are concerned with man as a creature of God, and as occupying a privileged position among all the things which have come into being. It is because man is a creature that there is light in him. It is lit in him by the divine Logos. The life that is in the Logos becomes the light of men. By "light" intelligence is meant. But though this light coincides with what we call intelligence, yet the orientation of the conception of light is nevertheless appreciably different. Intelligence in itself does not fall within the reckoning. The capacity of man to achieve great things by means of his intelligence is not in itself a recommendation: "For even if one is perfect among the sons of men, yet without the wisdom that comes from thee he will be regarded as nothing." (Wisd. of Sol. ix.6.)

According to Scripture there is light only in the man in communion with God.

But we must not think that the latter is an addendum, in the sense that man sets his intelligence to work, and in addition also believes in God. The light about which John is speaking is connected with the creation of man. It is possible for man to dowse this light. One goes on thinking and reasoning, but one's heart is darkened. "They became futile in their thinking and their senseless minds were darkened" is what St. Paul says about idolaters. (Rom. i.21.) Then man as creature of God collapses. Light, on the contrary, is the principle of growth and leads to life. It is itself life.

The light of intelligence, which the Bible locates in the heart, is here seen as the capacity of man to stand open to God. This is the way in which he is created by the Word, and this is the way of his completion. In this lies contained all other intellectual virtue. It is from the orientation to God, which constitutes the essence of man, that all human knowing derives its worth. Without this light he sees nothing, though he should investigate the whole world with his scientific insight.

"The light shines in the darkness, and the darkness has not overcome it." The darkness is the enemy of the light and is set upon extinguishing it, but has not succeeded. The verb "shine" is in the present tense. One can thus, noting especially 1 John ii.8, "the true light is already shining," reasonably hold that this verse refers to the incarnation of the Word. For the moment I shall not pursue this point. I wish to dwell for a moment on the conceptions of light and darkness, which throughout the Bible, but especially in the Fourth Gospel, are connected with good and evil.

John i.5 recalls Wisd. of Sol. vii.29-30:

> For she is more beautiful than the sun,
> and excels every constellation of the stars.
> Compared with light she is found to be superior,
> for it is succeeded by the night,
> but against wisdom evil does not prevail.

Wisdom is superior to the light of the visible world, since that light must cede to night. But Wisdom is overcome by no night, that is, by no evil. Compare John i.5, ". . . and the darkness has not overcome [the light] [of the Logos]."

Wisdom is seen as a light which excels the visible sunlight in splendour. We might think that we are here faced with a comparison according to which the interior light of man, which proceeds from Wisdom and the Logos, is called "light" by transference; but in fact the interior light of intelligence has nothing to do with the light outside man.

In the Bible the two forms of light are connected. The Hebrew conception of man plays a part here. In our culture, which is determined to a considerable degree by the natural sciences, the human faculty of sight is scientifically analysed as an object. In addition, a dualism contributes to separate the physiological activities of vision from the interior vision of the intellect. Modern philosophy has once more made it clear that human ocular vision is a spiritual act that differs from animal vision as man does from the animal. This intuition of the unity of man was possessed by the Israelites also. They saw the body as the exteriorization of the person, and physical vision as the exteriorization of inward vision.

The difference from philosophy is that, in the Bible, exterior seeing only gives light when the inner man is illuminated by communion with God. From the evil heart comes the "eye which is evil." (Mark vii.22.) True wisdom, which consists in doing the will of God, radiates from the eye. "The commandment of the Lord is pure, enlightening the eyes." (Ps. xix.8.)

In all the texts of the Fourth Gospel and of the first letter of John, where the inner light is mentioned, the way of representing it is borrowed from natural light. (John iii.19-21; viii.12; ix.2; v.35; xi.9-10; xii.35-6, 46; 1 John i.5-7; ii.8-11.) When Jesus says: "I am the light of the world," the words "the light of the world" sound precisely the same as in xi.9: "If any one walks in the day, he does not stumble, because he sees *the light of this world.*" The next verse continues: "But if any one walks in the night, he stumbles, because the light is not *in him.*"

One never knows exactly which the Evangelist is referring to: the inner or the outer light. The connection between the two forms of light is also greatly strengthened by the biblical notion of creation. We have more than once referred to the hymn to divine Wisdom which we find in Job xxviii. When God gave to the wind its weight, and meted out to the waters their measure, and made a decree for the rain, *then He saw Wisdom*. Here Wisdom is thought of as the power which carries and orders the universe. Only the Creator of the universe sees right through his creation and discerns his wisdom in it. It is the same Wisdom, called Logos by John, which carries man, too, with her creative power, but in the shape now of inward light. In man Wisdom rules the light of intelligence, the very Wisdom which is the foundation of all creation. The light of intelligence, which constitutes the essence of man, originates in Wisdom, which is itself "a pure emanation of the glory of the Almighty." (Wisd. of Sol. vii.26.)

This is the source of the "light of the world." It does not come from the sun, or the moon or the stars, but wells up in the heart of man. But the intelligence of man, as we have said, is light only when directed to God. Hence it is only for the man who stands open to God that the world is irradiated by light. Only he can walk in this world without stumbling. Only he sees creation as God's creation, because the light which is in him originates in God and goes back to God via the creation. A cosmonaut once declared that nowhere in space did he meet God. Such people will have to acknowledge the words that Wisd. of Sol. v.6 puts in the mouths of sinners at the day of judgment: "The light of righteousness did not shine on us, and the sun did not rise upon us."

The Gospel of John commences with the words "In the beginning," and in so doing refers back to the opening of the Book of Genesis: "In the beginning God made heaven and earth." Genesis then depicts for us a chaos over which the Spirit of God moved. Then God spoke his first creative word: "Let there be light." And there was light. It is the light of the divine Wisdom, the sending forth of the eternal Light, creating order in the abysmal chaos.

The poet of the Creation story is interpreting a thought common in the Wisdom literature: Yahweh formed Wisdom as the first of his works, as the first of his wonders of old. The first of the wonders of God's creation was concerned with Wisdom, "the beginning of God's creation." (Rev. iii.14.) Taken literally, these texts speak about the *creation* of Wisdom. Ecclus. i.4 directly says, "Wisdom was created before all things." The explanation of this way of speaking is that the writers of the Bible saw the bringing forth both of Wisdom and of Creation in a single perspective. God creates by uttering his word, and by radiating his wisdom, his completely original, eternal light, through everything. The divine light penetrates everywhere with the power of its purity: "Thy immortal spirit is in all things." (Wisd. of Sol. xii.1.)

In the beginning of creation the chaos is fructified by the Spirit of God moving over the abyss. The becoming-man of Wisdom commenced with the first incarnation of Wisdom in creation. Creation reaches its peak on the sixth day in the wonder of man, created after God's image and likeness, ruling over the earth and holding it subject, just because man has his life from God.

The light which, in Jesus, came to the world does not overwhelm the world. It is in the world as long as men are in the world, as intelligible light. The true light, that enlightens *every man, "was coming* into the world" (John i.9-11): "The true light that enlightens every man was coming into the world. He was in the world, and the world was made through him, yet the world knew him not." That Wisdom, which was present from the beginning of creation and was the ordaining creative power of God, comes, by the creation of man, to the surface in the form of the interior light of reason, in order at last to reveal itself as a person in the inner light of the man Jesus Christ. Yet the world did not recognize him. His own, whose light was dowsed by sin, did not acknowledge him. But then there sounds a new creative word: "For it is the God who said, 'Let light shine out of the darkness,' who has shone in our hearts to give the light of the knowledge of the glory of God in the face of Christ." (2 Cor. iv.6.) The light which through Jesus Christ now shines in the heart of the Apostle who brings the glad tidings *is the same light* which God evoked in the beginning of creation. Now, too, it occurs through a wrestling with chaotic darkness, but the victory is sure, "for the darkness has not overcome it."

The Son of God made man is the Light of the world. He was the eternal Wisdom who, before his becoming flesh, and in the time of preparation, "in every generation passed into holy souls, and made them friends of God, and prophets." (Wisd. of Sol. vii.27.) The godly of the Old Covenant lived by this light, and through this light praised God in his creation. For Wisdom does not enlighten only man but makes creation recognizable as God's creation by giving it form and order.

Before man existed Wisdom already inhabited the universe, and because the wisdom of God was in all things nothing was meaningless. Because of Wisdom those creatures who were never seen by man were not meaningless. They were there to praise their Creator. But as soon as man is raised by Wisdom to knowledge of the Creator he becomes the interpreter of the hymn of creation.

# 6

# THE HYMN OF CREATION

Père Teilhard de Chardin, in his much discussed and criticized book *The Phenomenon of Man,* says that we require new organs of perception in order to get a true view of the greatness and smallness of man. We need a sense for immeasurable space, a sense for the depth of time, a sense for the innumerable multiplicity of creatures, a sense for the relations of the unobservably small and the unimaginably great, a sense of the dynamics concealed under an exterior of rest. And, indeed, with these senses a new world opens for us. A most exciting drama unrolls before the spirit, in which man, too, takes on a new appearance.

If we are able to give a few simple facts to help us to orientate ourselves in this cosmic largeness, facts presented to us by science, we must not neglect to honour the human genius which, through science, has opened these perspectives to us.

We live on the planet earth, in the year 1965 of the Christian era. These 1964 years form a considerable portion of what we call historical time, which extends back a few thousand years BC. This period of more or less accessible human history forms a very small part of the period which separates us from the end of the Ice Age, and which must be estimated at more than a hundred centuries. The post-Ice-Age period is called the Alluvium, while the Ice Age is called the Diluvium. Alluvium and Diluvium together form the Quaternary, whose duration is reckoned at half a million to a million years. The existence of man on earth goes back to the beginning of this period.

Our capacity for representing to ourselves the passage of time begins to fail us here, and yet we are standing only on the threshold of the time which separates us from the origin of the earth. According to the compilation, *Das stammesgeschichtliche Werden der Organismen und des Menschen* (Herder, Freiburg [1959]), the main ages of the earth can be reckoned as follows in terms of duration: Quaternary, say, 1 million years; Tertiary, 60 million; Secondary, 125 million; Primary, 335 million. These periods add up to over half a milliard years. This is the period of time in which life on earth developed a boundless variety of plant and animal forms, while the most primitive forms of life go back to still earlier times. And we must not forget the Algonquian period, which precedes the periods mentioned, and which alone covers half a milliard years. The existence of life before the Algonquian is still a doubtful question for science. The German work mentioned dates the oldest animal life at 700 million years ago. As regards vegetable life, traces of plant life, according to the most recent investigations, must be estimated at 2700 million years old, though this cannot yet be regarded as decisively established.

In the time before that, there was no life on earth, which was preparing itself as a place for the life of plant and animal. The total age of our planet is estimated at from 5 to 7 milliard years.

The knowledge of ancient forms of life would provide uncertain material for a theory of evolution if these forms could not be chronologically arranged. The age of a fossil, the remains of a living being preserved in the earth, usually in petrified form, is deduced from the age of the stratum in which it is found. These strata are deposits which can be variously caused—for instance, by precipitates in the sea. They reach considerable thicknesses. In the Rhineland, which once lay under the sea, the successive layers deposited by the seawater from 400 to 200 million years ago reach a total thickness of 30,000 ft. Through later movements of the earth's crust and erosion these layers have in places come to the surface again. The age of these layers has been successfully calculated by measuring radioactivity.

After this descent into the depths of time, a word about the size of the universe. Astronomy, too, is greatly indebted to physics, a science without which it could not exist. In the description of what is found in space we can again go to work by steps.

One of the smallest systems of interdependent heavenly bodies is that of earth and the moon. The moon is the short mean distance of 238,860 miles from the earth. The light of the moon, which is reflected sunlight, reaches us in not much more than one second. Together with the other planets which we can clearly discern in the heavens (the morning or evening star, Venus, and also Mars, Saturn and Jupiter) and others which are harder to see, the earth moves round the sun, which is about 93 million miles from us, and whose light takes about eight minutes to reach us. Sun and planets, with their moons, form the solar system, which, in its turn, is part of a galaxy, to which practically everything belongs which we can see in the sky with the naked eye, notably, the pale band known traditionally as the Milky Way. The sun is one of the many stars in this galaxy. In cosmic space distances are so vast that measurement by miles has been supplanted by a scale taken from the speed that light, which travels at 186,000 miles per second, traverses in one year. This is called a light-year. The star which is nearest the sun is a good four light-years away. This distance is quite unimaginable, and yet we stand barely on the threshold of the universe. Together with this neighbouring star we are located somewhere in a spiral offshoot of the galaxy, of which we must think as of a revolving flattened disc, spiral in form and consisting of about 100 *milliard* stars. The length of this disc is reckoned at 80,000 light-years, the thickness at the middle at 16,000 light-years. Our galaxy is one of many in space, meaning by many, *milliards*. The number of these extra-galactic systems is to be compared with the number of stars in our galaxy.

Modern astronomical observations probe space to a distance of about 2 *milliard* light-years. Recently observation by means of light has been supplemented by radio-astronomy, by means of which the dark interstellar cosmic matter can also be observed. This "matter" far surpasses in quantity the mass of all the stars together, and is the womb out of which new stars are ever being born.

When we bring our thoughts back to the age of life on earth, we can connect the two dimensions by saying that the light which the astronomer, or better, his instruments, receives from the furthest observable system was emitted into space when the first life on earth had hardly begun to develop. To bring the unimaginable somewhat within the reach of our powers of representation, we can have recourse to a comparison. If we put the age of the earth at 5 milliard years, and then represent this time by one year, running from the 1st of January to the 31st of December, then according to the above estimates we must date the first appearance of plant life in the first half of July, and the origin of animal life approximately on the 10th of November. The million years of the Quaternary, in which man appears, begins at 22.40 hrs. on the 31st of December. The birth of Christ takes place twelve seconds before the end of our imaginary year. As to space, the portion of the universe which the man of the future is likely to reach is to the totality of astronomically ascertainable space as a speck of dust to the whole globe.

As against the unrepresentably great dimensions of cosmic space we have the unobservably small world of the atom, unreachable by direct optical observation. The German physicist Max Born wrote a popular work on the structure of the microcosm, the world of the small. It bore the title *The Unresting Universe.* Just as in the realm of the great, the macrocosm, everything is in movement, so the apparently dead and unmoving matter of our observation is in its ultimate structure a realm of unlimited movement. In addition to this restlessness we are struck, in the realm of the small, by the sparseness which characterizes it under an exterior of density and impenetrability. The volume of a battleship can theoretically be reduced to a few cubic centimetres. The unit of measurement applied to the section of the atomic nucleus is one quadrillionth of a square centimetre (1 with 24 noughts).

In the middle of a cosmos like this stands man. When he realizes what it is like, he puts himself the question: What, in this immensity, am I? And especially, who is this Jesus of Nazareth whom even his contemporaries doubted? What has this person to do with the extragalactic clouds, with their milliards of stars, and with the structure of the atom, in which the physicist is forever discovering new parts? And can it be possible that our Father in heaven has created all this?

We have duly taken note above of the extent of the universe. But advertence of this kind has not yet arrived at the level of knowledge. This is generated only by closer reflection, and through being actually concerned with the reality of the cosmos. For the theologian and for the faithful it is worth while to pick up a book containing photographs of the heavens by means of which the immeasurability of the galactic system and the presence of extragalactic clouds becomes somewhat graspable. Through reflection we must try to give some content to the conception of a light-year. We should meditate on the figures by means of which the size of the cosmos is described. Then perhaps we shall realize that there is a psychological connection between our belief in God as Creator and the notion which we have of the created universe. The attributes "omnipotent" and "infinite" which we ascribe to God then appear as abstract. Working with these abstract attributes, it may have suggested itself to us that the observation of cosmic space should be, for the astronomer, an occasion to praise God, and that it could bring the unbeliever to an acceptance of the existence of God. Actually, just the opposite is true. In an essay called "The Distance of the Andromeda Cloud"—a system more than a million light-years away—Romano Guardini relates of himself how becoming acquainted with the extent of the universe, through telescope and photos, enabled him to grasp how the representation of God could, through looking at the actual cosmos, become empty of content.

It would be interesting to trace, in the history of revelation and of the believing consciousness, how the perception of the greatness of God arose, not from abstract conceptions, but from the concrete manifestation of his power in a particular area. In the beginning of the story of revelation

Yahweh was the God of a clan. When David fled before Saul to the desert of Ziph, and was pursued by him, he said: "If it is men [who have stirred you up against me] may they be cursed before the Lord, for they have driven me out this day that I should have no share in the heritage of the Lord, saying: 'Go, serve other gods.' Now therefore, let not my blood fall to the earth away from the presence of the Lord." (1 Sam. xxvi.19-20.) Jonah wished to flee to Tarshish "from the presence of the Lord." (Jonah i.3.) The Book of Jonah aims at teaching the reader that God is powerful everywhere on earth. Thus does the consciousness of the extent of God's power expand in the believer. He is adored as the Creator of heaven and earth conceived as the overarching space of the old world-image. Today we have to learn that God's dominion extends to the extragalactic clouds.

We can cross this threshold by going back to the biblical conception of creation through a Wisdom which communicates itself to man in the light of reason. It is the "light of the world" which, in present-day astronomy, probes the world in the endless depths of her space and time. That reason can "see" all this is due to the visibility given to all creatures by the indwelling wisdom of God, the same Wisdom which is operative in human reason too. And then what is there against accepting that Wisdom may, in one Man, so overwhelm reason, that she is herself the person expressing herself in the human intelligence?

Another question which the believer puts concerns the

sense of all this. What sense can one make of the spiral nebulae beyond extragalactic observation, in a space towards which the furthest observable clouds are receding from us at a speed of more than 30,000 miles per second? What sense has the turmoil of the cosmic powers in the interior of the stars, an area which will always remain closed to men? What sense do the vanished species of animals make which inhabited our earth hundreds of millions of years ago? What sense, too, the millions of beings, each one more fantastic than the last, which radiate their light in the absolute darkness of deep ocean, light which will never be seen by human eye?

It is impressive, this parade of animals which, in the place where we now live, battled and fought, and no man present. From the Cambrian, the period of the earth from 520 to 440 million years ago, thousands of animals have been described from fossils, and the number is still increasing. All the main phyla of animal life are already present, except the vertebrates, and these already appear in the Silurian (410-320 million years ago). The further history of life is characterized by refining, completing and shifting modifications in the basic plan, accompanied by the constant appearance of new kinds, which can be classified into ever new groups. For the small island of Jutland alone more than two thousand kinds of animals are noted in connection with the Silurian period. That a particular animal species arises does not imply that it will keep itself going. During the Cambrian half the animal kingdom consisted of numerous forms of trilobites, which died out wholly in the Permian (218-185 million years ago). The same holds for the giant reptiles which catch our attention by their immense size. These rulers of land, water and air reached a high point in the Cretaceous period (130-60 million) and died out in the same period.

To the vertebrate animals, to which man is most closely related biologically, belong fishes, the amphibians (which always formed a comparatively small group), the reptiles, the mammals and the birds. This summary corresponds with the order of their appearance in time: the fishes in the Silurian, the amphibians in the Carboniferous period (265-210 million), the mammals more or less in the transition from the Triassic to the Jurassic (155 million). The birds appear about the same time. The mammals appear as marsupials, producing embryos which are fed in a pouch; and as placental mammals, nourishing the embryos in the womb until they are capable of independent existence. Of these, the insectivorous mammals are the oldest representatives. They appear towards the end of the Cretaceous period (60 million).

This brings us to the Tertiary, when, according to scientific terminology, a new period of animal life dawns, the Neozoic, which represents a tremendous development of placental mammals. In the comparatively short time of the Quaternary (short in comparison with the preceding periods), which is characterized by a succession of cold waves, there appear in Europe kinds of animal confined to the cold periods: the cave bear, the woolly rhinoceros, the mammoth, and others. Only from now onwards do animals live under the eye of man.

Evolution presents itself as the aimless unfolding of life. It is hard to discern direction to a goal. The strangest animals come into being and die out. It is possible to talk, as Simpson does, about the fantastically complicated structure of general evolution. Man, who feels himself to be the measure of things, finds it difficult to assimilate all this. The believer feels himself to be excluded from the counsels of God. Here he is ignorant as was Job, brought to understanding by Yahweh in a whirlwind:

> Where were you when I laid the foundation of
>   the earth?
> Tell me, if you have understanding.
> Who determined its measurements—surely you
>   know!
> Or who stretched the line upon it?
> On what were its bases sunk,
> or who laid its cornerstone,
> when the morning stars sang together,
> and all the sons of God shouted for joy?
> Or who shut in the sea with doors,
> when it burst forth from the womb;
> when I made clouds its garment,
> and thick darkness its swaddling-band,
> and prescribed bounds for it,
> and set bars and doors,

and said, "Thus far shalt thou come, and no
farther,
and here shall your proud waves be stayed"?
Have you commanded the morning since your
days began,
and caused the dawn to know its place,
that it might take hold of the skirts of the earth,
and the wicked be shaken out of it?
It is changed like clay under the seal,
and it is dyed like a garment.
From the wicked their light is withheld,
and their uplifted arm is broken.
Have you entered into the springs of the sea,
or walked in the recesses of the deep?
Have the gates of death been revealed to you,
or have you seen the gates of deep darkness?
Have you comprehended the expanse of the
earth?
Declare, if you know all this.

[Job. xxxviii.4-18]

Man is silenced. But the wonders of God did not go unwitnessed. The wisdom of God was present:

The Lord created me at the beginning of his
work,
the first of his acts of old.
Ages ago I was set up,
at the first, before the beginning of the earth.

When there were no depths I was brought
forth,
when there were no springs abounding with
water.
Before the mountains had been shaped,
before the hills, I was brought forth;
before he had made the earth with its fields,
or the first of the dust of the world.
When he established the heavens, I was there,
when he drew a circle on the face of the deep,
when he assigned to the sea its limit,
so that the waters might not transgress his command,
when he marked out the foundations of the
earth,
then I was beside him, like a master workman;
and I was daily his delight,
rejoicing before him always,
rejoicing in his inhabited world,
and delighting in the sons of men.

[Prov. viii.22-31]

The creation is divine play. Now that we are better able to penetrate the earth's primeval time, this biblical idea becomes particularly impressive:

O Lord, how manifold are thy works!
In Wisdom hast thou made them all:
the earth is full of thy creatures.
Yonder is the sea, great and wide,

which teems with things innumerable,
living things, both small and great.
There go the ships,
and Leviathan which thou didst form to sport
in it.
These all look to thee,
to give them their food in due season.
When thou givest to them, they gather it up;
when thou openest thy hand,
they are filled with good things.
When thou hidest thy face, they are dismayed;
when thou takest away their breath, they die
and return to their dust.
When thou sendest forth thy Spirit, they are
created,
and thou renewest the face of the ground.

[Ps. civ.24-30]

In the hundreds of millions of years which preceded the birth of man, Wisdom played upon the earth under the eyes of God. Wisdom, which in the first beginning descended upon the chaos under the lifegiving breath of God, has ever since sung to the Creator a song without words: the hymn of the creation. She has celebrated a cosmic liturgy, to delight at last amongst the sons of men, and to interpret her hymn in a human voice:

I came forth from the mouth of the Most High,
and covered the earth like a mist.

I dwelt in high places,
and my throne was in a pillar of cloud.
Alone I have made the circuit of the vault of
heaven
and have walked in the depths of the abyss.
In the waves of the sea, in the whole earth,
and in every people and nation I have gotten
a possession.
Among all these I sought a resting place;
I sought in whose territory I might lodge.

Then the Creator of all things gave me a commandment,
and the one who created me assigned a place
for my tent.
And he said, "Make your dwelling in Jacob,
and in Israel receive your inheritance."
From eternity, in the beginning, he created me,
and for eternity I shall not cease to exist.
In the holy tabernacle I ministered before him,
and so I was established in Zion.
In the beloved city likewise he gave me a resting
place,
and in Jerusalem was my dominion.
So I took root in an honoured people,
in the portion of the Lord, who is their
inheritance.

[Ecclus. xxiv.3-12]

Here the poet is speaking about the solemn service in the Temple of Jerusalem. The liturgy of the People of God continues the liturgy of the creation. Man knows himself to have the closest ties with visible creation when he stands before God in the sanctuary. The liturgical chants of Israel are preserved for us in the Psalms. They enable us still to bear witness of human praise in the name of creation, as that sounded in the Temple of Jerusalem centuries before the coming of Christ:

O sing to the Lord a new song;
sing to the Lord, all the earth!
Sing to the Lord, bless his name;
tell of his salvation from day to day.
Declare his glory among the nations,
his marvellous works among all the peoples!
For great is the Lord, and greatly to be praised;
he is to be feared above all gods.
For all the gods of the peoples are idols;
but the Lord made the heavens.
Honour and majesty are before him;
strength and beauty are in his sanctuary.
Ascribe to the Lord, O families of the peoples,
ascribe to the Lord glory and strength!
Ascribe to the Lord the glory due his name;
bring an offering, and come into his courts!
Worship the Lord in holy array;
tremble before him, all the earth!

Say among the nations, "The Lord reigns!
Yea, the world is established, it shall never be
  moved;
he will judge the peoples with equity."
Let the heavens be glad, and let the earth
  rejoice;
let the sea roar, and all that fills it;
let the field exult, and everything in it!
Then shall all the trees of the wood sing for
  joy
before the Lord, for he comes,
for he comes to judge the earth.
He will judge the world with righteousness,
and the peoples with his truth.

[Ps. xcvi]

# 7

# THE BIBLICAL VIEW OF MAN

Man was created by God to be sovereign over creation by seeing it as God's creation; that is, by seeing it in its reference to him who alone is to be worshipped, and who will tolerate no false gods in his presence. Human history shows that men have set up idols. Instead of being lord of creation, man has become its slave, looking to it for the satisfaction of his longing for eternal life. God has willed to restore man to his lordship over creation and to give this lordship an imperishable form. He sent his Son so that creation should be subject in a new and definitive way, not as formerly to the man of dust, but to the heavenly man.

Now that the heavenly man has appeared, the full misery of the man of dust is revealed. It is now apparent not only that as creature he is still awaiting his perfection, but more especially that he is imprisoned by the powers of death and sin. By the aid of a few central texts of Holy Scripture I shall attempt to describe this situation. Here is the point of departure for the greatest work which God has done in his creation; the uplifting of man from his last state to a sharing in his own glory and in his dominion over creation.

In his Letter to the Romans, St. Paul speaks with great emphasis of the evil condition of all mankind as a consequence of the fate in which we are involved through the lordship of sin and death. Of outstanding interest is the well-known text of Rom. v.11 where we see the personified powers of sin and death entering the world in triumph after the sin of Adam. A precise understanding of these and other passages requires that, before we undertake our exegesis, we first get some clear idea of the conceptions of sin and death in their relation to each other.

When we were outlining broadly the Old Testament view of the moral order as an aspect of the created order, we came to a point where we said that here the concepts of death and life were first found. Man, in withdrawing himself from the commands of God, enters the domain of death. This follows from the fact that God's commands are creative. Man's disobedience brings blindness with it. Here again our mode of knowing is connected with our moral attitude, though everything is now negative. Just as the righteous man, who is obedient to God, experiences his presence by knowledge and the inward light, so the heart of the man who withholds due honor from God is totally darkened. (Rom. i.19-21.)

In this way death acquires a deeper actuality than the physical occurrences which we can observe. Because death stands essentially in the sign of man's refusal to accept

God's creative will, its visible, physical side becomes secondary.

In the yet incomplete insight of the wise men of the Old Testament, the concept of death does not yet achieve the profundity found in the New Testament. The doctrine of this-worldly rewards implies that death, though in the first place a breaking of the communion with Yahweh, is in large measure the loss of those things which fill this life with pleasant experience. With the dawn of a doctrine of rewards beyond the grave, the earthly success of our lives becomes completely relative. It is interesting to see how the writers of the Book of Wisdom cannot say enough about this, particularly in Chapters 3 and 4. They wish to say that now the righteous can *live,* even though they lack all worldly goods; yes, even though they are done to death by the enemies of God. But the sinner has no future on which he can build. His worldly prosperity will finally desert him. He will then become a corpse forever. (iv. 19.)

> After this they will become dishonoured corpses,
> and an outrage among the dead for ever;
> because he will dash them speechless to the ground,
> and shake them from the foundations;
> they will be left utterly dry and barren,
> and they will suffer anguish,
> and the memory of them will perish.

This is the consciously experienced eschatological death, here depicted as unnatural disharmony. When St. Paul in

Eph. ii.1-5 reminds his readers of the condition in which they—and he—were before they knew Christ, he speaks of those who are dead in sin and error. Their condition is described by the word *nekros,* which in ordinary usage meant "dead." This is no metaphor unless it be that "dead" here sounds more real than in its everyday use. Sinners are dead because they revolt against creation. This death situation is the total denial of a created good, namely, life, which should have been there.

We are disposed to reduce conceptions such as joy, grief, love, hate and despair to a sphere in which our existence as creatures is not involved. They are conditions of a spirit which, as created reality or as immaterial substance, is not subject to breaking down or building up. The body has little to do with such conceptions, and the world about us, nothing. Yet in all these spiritual conditions we have to do with man in the actuality of his created status. Our insight into the true state of affairs can be clarified if we reflect that man has the task of integrating into his personality the body, which must be accepted as a given dimension of his existence. The subject realizes himself by achieving freedom in the body, by personalizing the body. This task, which characterizes earthly man, implies that man can go in two directions. Either he achieves this personalizing of the body, or he becomes the victim of his bodily existence which, without this personalizing, is liable to fall back onto the animal level. It can then happen that superficially he can be said to be "enjoying life," but no completion of his humanity is taking place. Internally the man is destroying himself.

The foregoing sentences have been dictated to us by modern philosophy, but this philosophy can help us to understand the Pauline notion of death. By its aid it becomes clearer to us that Paul could call the pagan hedonists dead in a very real sense, even though outwardly they looked anything but dead. At the point where man is most fully man—that is, at the point where his life arises out of a meeting with God—there death can irrupt to break down man as a creature of God. Here death can become a condition, a way of existing, which gives birth to "dead works." (Heb. vi.1; ix.14.)

Thus when the time allotted to man to make something of himself has passed, his internal condition stands revealed in eschatological life or eschatological death.

The concept of death developed here is the key to the way Paul thinks in Rom. v.12-21, of which we quote the first three verses only: "[12] Therefore, as sin came into the world through one man and death through sin, and so death spread to all men because all men sinned—[13] sin indeed was in the world before the law was given, but sin is not counted where there is no law. [14] Yet death reigned from Adam to Moses, even over those whose sins were not like the transgression of Adam, who was a type of the one who was to come."

Verse 12 forms the first part of a full sentence which

breaks off in the middle. A new clause should now begin, introduced by "so" to correspond with the "as" at the beginning: "as through one man [Adam] . . . so through one man [Christ] . . ." By violating the ordinance of God, Adam introduced sin into the world, and death as a consequence of sin. Sin and death are introduced as personified forces which take possession of the world. Subsequently it is said of death that *he spread to all men.* The event has taken place, and all men are under the power of death. The proof of this is the evidence: all men have sinned. Here Paul picks up the conclusion again, at which he arrived in iii.23 after subjecting the behaviour of pagans and Jews to a critical judgment: "All have sinned and fall short of the glory of God." This conclusion now serves as an argument to indicate the universal reign of death. Sin, which reigns everywhere, makes plain that all men are "dead." Dead works bear witness to the death in which humanity is involved.

In the interpretation of Rom. v.12-14, exegesis usually follows the sequence sin-death, which is given at the beginning of *v.* 5, and, for the rest, is known to occur throughout the Bible. But this sequence does not hold for the second half of *v.* 12. The aorist "has spread" indicates a completed fact, that this fact is proved by experience. The presence of death betrays itself in sin: "By their fruits shalt thou know them."

After this, the exegesis of *vv.* 13-14 becomes comparatively simple. When Paul declares in *v.* 12 that all have sinned, he is thinking of the people whose behaviour he has criticized in i.18-iii.20. They are people of his own time. But one could ask: Has death *always* reigned? Did the people of earlier times also sin? This problem becomes particularly acute in connection with Paul's statement in Rom. iv.15: "Where there is no law, there is no transgression." Hence the question: Were the people who lived before the law all sinners? Connecting with the last words of *v*. 12, "all men sinned," Paul immediately says that before the Law, also, there was sin in the world. "All men sinned" thus becomes an absolutely general statement. The story of the Flood, and that of the destruction of Sodom and Gomorrah, tell a plain tale. In Gen. vi the universality of sin is affirmed in so many words.

But now Paul introduces his own principle, where there is no law there is no transgression, as an objection: No sin is imputed where there is no law. Yet there was sin in the world before the Law. The only possible explanation of this must be found in the fact that death reigned. The sins of olden days are betrayed by the rule of death. "Yet death reigned from Adam to Moses, even over those whose sins were not like the transgression of Adam, who was a type of the one who was to come." (Rom. v.14.) Here it appears that men can sin without the Law. (Rom. ii.12.) Death held sway over the people of primitive times, too, as one can see from their sins. This primitive dominion of death finds its final explanation in the trespass of Adam. Through his sin Adam brought death into the world. Hence, right from the beginning of human history the principle has full validity: where there is no law, there is no sin. Adam did not die because of a natural principle of death in him. His sin can only be explained as the breaking of a law.

Paul's reasoning implies that Adam is responsible for the actual situation. The image of misery that the world presents is attributed by the Apostle to the reign of death initiated by Adam through his sin.

In addition we should note a few points of interest before setting out our own position. If we enquire on what point Paul concentrates his interest, we find that it is centred on the universal rule of death and the consequent universality of sin. The universality of sin was also the conclusion of his first demonstration, which did not start with Adam but with experience, a demonstration which he sets out in the first chapters of the letter. In fact the argument returns again in v. 12, and it is not so much Adam as the experience of the universality of sin which leads to the acceptance of the necessity of salvation.

The essential revelation of the condition of man has its source not so much in the story of Paradise as in the consideration of the redeeming suffering of Christ. What man is, is revealed by the crucifixion and resurrection of Jesus, and so is what man may be in the future by God's grace. Beyond human possibility God's righteousness has been revealed. "But now the righteousness of God has been manifested apart from law, although the law and the prophets bear witness to it, the righteousness of God through faith in

Jesus Christ for all who believe. For there is no distinction, since all have sinned and fallen short of the glory of God." (Rom. iii.21-3.) Whoever understands God's work of salvation in this manner must accept that *man* is powerless to work his own salvation. The Cross reveals the helplessness and lostness of man. The scriptural proof from Gen. ii-iii is used as an illustration.

It is also of interest to note that, in the Letter to the Romans, Paul intertwines two methods of argument, so that his pronouncements seem to be contradictory. One can posit it as a principle that the salvific work of Christ excludes the intrinsic righteousness of man. It follows from this that *nobody* is found righteous by God. The whole world stands accused. Next to this there is *history in the concrete,* which after all presents another picture. There were righteous men of old, even under the Law. Rom. ii.12-16 does not exclude the possibility that there are pagans who find the path to God. In Rom. i-iii Paul proceeds to derive, from the historical argument, the basic position which he formulates in iii.19: that the whole world is accountable to God. Strictly speaking, this position can never be proved from experience. It can be concluded only from the consideration of the work of salvation. It then becomes clear that the righteous men of old, and of now, could and can be righteous only by virtue of the salvific work of Christ, because the latter reveals that man himself is impotent.

In conclusion we notice that the statement of the influence of Adam on his descendants remains in the background. No mention is made of an influence exercised by the propagation of the human race. The connecting link is death personified, which only becomes operative in man, who has knowledge of good and evil. Among the exegetes the opinion is gaining ground that Paul was not considering the case of the newly born child but was giving his attention to man as he appears in the course of his life. From this point we can establish a connection with Rom. vii.7-13 where man, before his confrontation with the Law, is represented as "living." It is true that according to Eph. ii.3 man in himself is disposed to the wrath which inevitably descends on him, but the point of departure of this fatal development need not yet be depicted by means of death in the pregnant sense of the word. In the course of his awakening to moral consciousness man encounters the powers which Adam introduced. We find the same layout in 1 Cor. xv.42-8. In *vv.* 45-9 present human existence is described in terms of Gen. ii.7, where the *creation* of Adam is spoken of. The man of today is, like Adam, earthly, he is "flesh and blood," and as such he cannot inherit the Kingdom of God. In this text sin still plays no part in the description of man. Yet later we see death and sin enter, and then Jesus Christ is named as he through whom we attain to victory.

Thus what we said in Chapter 3 about original sin appears to agree with St. Paul's teaching. According to the Apostle man is delivered over to sin and death, which rule the world as tyrannical powers; together with this there is in him the opposition of "the flesh." These two causes of personal sin, the one external and the other internal, naturally have a connection with one another. The body was not created by God as the "body of this death" (Rom. vii.24), but this is what it became under the influence of sin and death which rule in the world. The naturally given, though not in itself sinful, incapacity of man to reach his own perfection and inherit the Kingdom of God is prevented, by the powers which rule the world, from answering to the call from the side of God which is uttered to man in the Law. The Law, which should have led to life, now leads to death. (Rom. vii.10.) Liberation from this condition comes to sinful man only by the grace of God through the mediation of Christ.

Several points are confirmed by a comparison with Wisd. of Sol. i-ii. We find memories, in the Letters of Paul, of the Book of Wisdom. The plan of Rom. i is wholly constructed upon that of Wisd. of Sol. 13-14. From the consideration of creation man can come to a knowledge of the Creator. Idolatry is the beginning of the lapse (Wisd. of Sol. xiv.12), which propagates itself in all kinds of moral aberrations, including unnatural unchastity. (Wisd. of Sol. xiv.26.) There is no doubt that the Book of Wisdom sets the pattern for Paul's interpretation of Gen. ii-iii. However, in this matter we also find a notable difference. While, according to Rom. v.12, sin and death, as a result of Adam's trespass, triumphantly enter the world to lay siege to it, yet, according to Wisd. of Sol. i.14-15, the realm of death has no royal dominion on earth because "righteousness is immortal."

But the difference is more apparent than real and is completely to be explained by the fact that the author of Wisdom did not yet know about the atoning death of Jesus. He kept to the facts as he knew them, and confirms that in this world there are sinful and righteous men. That the righteous are righteous by virtue of the coming sufferings of the Messiah plays no part in his argument. Of course he knows that God is concerned with men. (i.2-5; vii.27, etc.) But in contrast with Romans, he represents death as having made its appearance in the world after the events in paradise, but without becoming a compelling power. Righteousness is immortal, and the righteous are not touched by this death. The sinner consciously calls down death upon himself. (i.15-16.) It is thus a historical way of looking at things: the fact is that man is himself responsible for choosing life or death, exactly as Jesus Son of Sirach had previously remarked: "Before a man are life and death, and whichever he chooses will be given to him." (Ecclus. xv. 14-17.) As we said, Paul was acquainted with these ideas: "When Gentiles who have not the law do by nature what the law requires, they are a law to themselves, even though they do not have the law. They show that what the law requires is written on their hearts, while their conscience also bears witness and their conflicting thoughts accuse or perhaps excuse them on that day when, according to my gospel, God judges the secrets of men by Christ Jesus." (Rom. ii.14-16.)

This exposition based on Rom. v.12-14, in which Paul describes the power of destiny over man, can be further extended by the exegesis of Paul's view of the destiny of creation, as we find it in Rom. viii.19-23, again with an application to Genesis. (iii.17.) What is the significance of saying that creation is subjected to a meaningless existence, and that it waits on its liberation from the slavery of what passes away?

Paul is speaking here about the *ktisis,* the creation, the same creation which in Rom. i is the point of departure for the knowledge of God. One could translate Rom. i.20: "*From the creation of the world* his invisible being is seen by reason in his works," where *ktisis* in the active sense refers to the creative action of God. In any event, the *ktisis* of i.25 is once more the given actuality of creation, as in Rom viii (and everywhere else in the New Testament). The exegesis of Rom. viii.19-23 is greatly clarified if we take the related passage in Rom. i.18-25 into consideration. Again and again we find the same ideas. First, the word *ktisis* or "creation." Secondly, futility: Rom. viii.20 says that creation is subjected to futility: in Rom. i.21 it is said of the Gentiles that they became futile in their thinking. The bondage to decay to which creation, according to viii.21, is subjected corresponds with the fact that the Gentiles have adored the creature instead of the Creator (i.25) and have thus exchanged the majesty of the *eternal* God for images resembling mortal man or birds or animals or reptiles. (i.23.) Thus the Gentiles adored the creatures which pass away, and passed by the Creator.

The comparison between the two passages suggests the thought that the futility and slavery to decay to which creation is, in Rom. viii, said to be subject represents a situation similar to that which follows from the cult of idols. If the Gentiles had come to the knowledge and service of the true God, creation would not have been subject to the slavery of decay. Creation would then have been for the Gentiles a way to God. But now this way has been cut off, and man directs himself to the creature, in order to serve it instead of the Creator. What comes of this the prophet Jeremiah had already pithily expressed. He, too, is acquainted with the notion that the people "have changed their glory for that which doth not profit" (ii.11), and declares in the name of Yahweh that he who pursues worthless things becomes worthless himself. (ii.5.) He who serves God, the fountain of living waters (ii.13), achieves life. He who idolizes the creature destroys himself. In the Septuagint the terminology of Jer. ii.5 is the same as that of Rom. i and viii.

In his pronouncements concerning the futility and slavery to decay to which creation is subject, Paul undoubtedly wishes to say that there is no future for creation while idolatry persists. The cause of this lies in man, who, instead of turning to the true God and thus putting himself beyond decay, couples himself with the creature which perishes. But it is the intention of God that creation shall share in the permanence of the man who serves God. This way has now been cut off because man serves the creature, and can thus never emerge above decay. That is why creation remains confined within its own decay. In addition it becomes futile, because it is the object of a futile cultus.

In the preceding, we have interpreted Rom. i and viii in the light of each other. Strictly taken, Rom. viii does not directly deal with idolatry, but with the events in the paradise of Eden. Yet the relation of the two pericopes remains. But then the relation between Rom. i and Rom. viii is exactly the same as that between Rom. i-iii and Rom. v.12-14; in other words, an argument from Scripture is put forward for what has previously been laid down by the analysis of history. The futility and the slavery of decay have overwhelmed creation because of the trespass of Adam. When Paul writes that creation has been subjected to futility, he uses the aorist tense to indicate a past occurrence. Undoubtedly he is thinking of the curse which God pronounced upon the earth after the sin of the first human couple. Creation wishes to ascend, but is hindered by the curse which has been pronounced on her against her will. Right up to the present day the creation groans in labour, but her rebirth is still postponed. Yet the dawning is come, because the children of God possess the firstfruits of the Spirit, and where the Spirit of God is, there is freedom. This freedom of the children of God will finally be revealed in their resurrection. Then creation too will show itself clearly as the creation of God.

The story of Genesis brings the same connection to view. God forms man "of the dust of the earth," then breathes the breath of life into his nostrils, and in this way man becomes a living being. (ii.7.) It is striking that the creation of man follows a different course from that of the plants and animals. (ii.9, 19.) In the case of the plants and animals, only the earth is named and not the dust. Also, it is not said that the breath of their life is breathed into them. God does not share his breath with these beings. In this way great emphasis is laid on the double character of man; he is of the dust, and he is related to God. Man is commissioned to *till* and keep the earth. The earth is entrusted to him as a planted garden. (ii.15.) The superiority of man over the lower beings is indicated by the fact that he names the animals, and finds below him not a single creature who can come to meet him and be a partner to help him. Then woman is created out of man. This act already points forward to the mystery of marriage in which man and wife return to a unity. The man and his wife are both naked without feeling shame. They possess themselves in perfect harmony.

This ideal state of affairs is dissolved as a consequence of the disobedience of the man and his wife and changed into a disorder. The man withdraws himself from the love of the Creator. He experiences this immediately in the shame which his nakedness now arouses. He hides from God. But God calls him to account and pronounces sentence. The relation of the man to the woman becomes one of domination, to which the woman has to subject herself whether she likes it or not. Further, the relation of man to the earth is changed. The earth is no longer a paradise, but a country from which man must wrest a living through toil and hardship.

What is particularly interesting in this representation is the relation of man to the earth. Through ii.5 the thought echoes that, before man's creation, the earth, as it were, cried out for someone to cultivate it. The cultivation of the earth is something close to the heart of the writer; it is the commission given to man after his creation. (ii.15.) Man must not only cultivate the land, but keep or preserve it. It is put wholly within the hand of man.

Man himself belongs to this earth. He is kneaded from the dust of the earth. But he is formed above it by the divine breath of life which is breathed into him, and because of which he is presented with the lordship over the world in which he stands. But all of this hangs upon the thread of his obedience. If he loses his grip upon God, then he falls back upon the earth from which he has so recently arisen. And this is the concrete situation in which the writer now finds man. He uses the divine sentence as an explanation of the actual situation. Man is a toiler without prospects: "In the sweat of your face you shall eat bread till you return to the ground, for out of it you were taken; you are dust, and to dust you shall return." (iii.19.) Therefore the Lord God sent him forth from the Garden of Eden, "to till the ground from which he was taken." (iii.23.) The writer insists upon the idea that man must cultivate the soil from which he was taken. This soil is now a garden no longer, but a cursed earth. When he described the creation of man, the writer let it appear that man was made of "dust." This datum now returns, after the tempter has in the meanwhile been described as an animal that eats dust. (iii.4.) In the sentence of Yahweh (iii.19) man is described as pure dust: the life-breath of Yahweh has ebbed out of the dust. After man has disobeyed the commandment he is a dead man. Now there remains nothing but dust which will vanish without trace in the earth. And the man who is now nothing but dust struggles with an earth which, through his fault, has ceased to be a garden planted by God and become a refractory soil in which man sows the plants of the fields and reaps thistles. (iii.18.)

We should be definitely wrong if we interpreted the ideas contained in the paradise story as if we were enquiring after the essence of man and of things, on the assumption that we could regard them as self-contained entities definable in themselves. In Holy Scripture we have always to do with the reciprocal relations of God and man. Outside of this relation there is theologically nothing to be said about man. When God breathes the breath of life into the dust which he has formed into a man, this breath of life is more than a principle of life by which man, considered in himself, lives. In the action is contained the assertion that man lives by God. Hence his place in the garden; his surroundings are made through and through by God. Man possessed lordship over things precisely because he lived by God.

Then he broke the command. He set himself over against his Creator and returned to dust. He then lost his lordship over the world, which became inimical to him. He is dead although he still goes about on earth. Access to the truth of life is barred. God drives man out of the Garden and appoints watchers to keep him from the Tree of Life.

This last narration depicts the situation of man as the writer of this sublime story sees it actually to be in the present world. The last sentence of the story reveals what the writer was dealing with: "He drove out the man; at the east of the garden of Eden he placed the cherubim, and a flaming sword which turned every way, to guard the way to the tree of life." (iii.24.) In the depths of his heart man possesses something eternal and without end, something which gives him a resemblance to God. It was instilled into him with the breath of life breathed into him from the mouth of God. On the other hand, man is not able to fulfil his longing for the Tree of Life. He wanders round over the earth, which returns no answer to his question. He returns to dust—i.e., here and now, the earth is all he lives for—and he vanishes.

Thus this view of man is constructed out of two components: the inner longing for eternity and the impotence to fulfil this longing. The two components are interpreted in one dramatic happening, by means of which they are illuminated in their separation, to be united again in the conclusion. The two together show what man is: a wanderer who, in the depths of his heart, longs for the Tree of Life, but sees that the gate is closed. We know now that Christ has opened this gate. Christians "have confidence to enter the sanctuary by the blood of Jesus, by the new and living way which he opened for us through the curtain, that is, through his flesh." (Heb. x.19-20.)

The slavery of decay to which St. Paul in Rom. viii sees creation subjected is thus strikingly illustrated by the story of paradise. The root of this decay does not lie in the creation. The writers of the New Testament do not have any doubts about the goodness of creation. Paul does not either: for him it remains a reference to God. Against its desire, and against its true nature and destination, creation is subjected by God to decay, to punish man for his transgression. This punishment is in its turn nothing other than the inevitable consequence of the attitude of disobedience to God taken up by man. When today we experience the forces of nature as a menace, it is as a consequence of the evilness of man, who is false to his longing for the infinite and abiding. Then, in his existence, he falls back into the dust from which he was taken, to vanish into it without trace, because what God does not know as his own has no meaning.

All those things have vanished like a shadow,
and like a rumour that passes by;

like a ship that sails through the billowy water,
and when it has passed, no trace can be found,
nor track of its keel in the waves;
or as, when a bird flies through the air,
no evidence of its passage is found;
the light air, lashed by the beat of its pinions
and pierced by the force of its rushing flight,
is traversed by the movement of its wings,
and afterwards no sign of its coming is found there;
or as, when an arrow is shot at a target,
the air, thus divided, comes together at once,
so that no one knows its pathway.
So we also, as soon as we were born, ceased to be,
and we had no sign of virtue to show,
but were consumed in our wickedness.

[Wisd. of Sol. 9-13]

The man who rejects God denies his permanence and confirms his transience. He does it by serving the creature and passing the Creator by. The existential interweaving of man and the world has the consequence that man, by betraying the urge to eternity in his heart, involves the world also in his transience.

The notion of an historical paradise, and an historical pair of progenitors who possessed paradisal privileges in the beginning and threw them away by breaking a concrete commandment—this idea I consider to be incompatible with an evolutionary picture of the world. But at the same time I wholly defend what, in the exegesis above, I indicated to be the intention of the sacred writers. They interpret for us the revelation about the condition of man under God. And this, after all, is what, finally, we have to do with in the dogma of original sin. The teaching authority of the Church has always guarded this dogma with vigilance. It has had to beat off attacks from the right and from the left, in which what was always involved was the relation of the teaching about original sin to Christ's work of salvation.

The writer of Genesis ii-iii is particularly impressed by the contradictions which he observes in man. Although man longs to live eternally, he vanishes into the earth of which he is formed. St. Paul describes the contrast in his own way in the famous passage in Rom. vii.14-25: man assents to the Law, but discovers in his members another law which has the upper hand.

The sense of this contrast has been a preoccupation of men quite apart from revelation. Plato realized that the spirit is greater than the body permits it to be. But whoever, like him, seeks to solve the riddle of man by means of a dualism of a good soul and an evil matter immediately creates therewith and in principle an absurd dualism of two antagonistic worlds. The visible creation, as became apparent in later Platonizing and gnostic movements, is no longer recognized as God's creation. The redemption of our bodies (Rom. viii.23) becomes a redemption from our bodies.

Yet the intuition of the contrast between spirit and body which Plato possessed had very close affinities to the biblical thought that the spirit is willing but the flesh is weak. To describe the contrast the author of Wisdom even uses Platonic terminology (ix.15):

> for a perishable body weighs down the soul,
> and his earthly tent burdens the thoughtful mind.

Here everything depends on whether one maintains the unity of man or not, whether one degrades the visible creation or continues to appreciate it as created good by God. If, in determining the contrast, one continues to affirm the unity, it follows that the fragile physical state of man is seen as co-determining his moral attitude. Man is a unity, and the physical and moral orders both embrace the whole of human existence as inseparable aspects of it. That is why his precarious physical condition is associated with a moral attitude characterized by weakness and instability. The biblical writers conclude from the physical weakness and mortality of man to his moral imperfection. Very telling in this connection is the description of human existence in Job xiv; life is short and full of trouble, man's life unfolds and withers; and a being like this challenges the judgment of God! Can what is clean come from what is unclean? From this it appears that the weakness of man, physical as well as moral, is regarded as innate. The well-known phrase of Ps. li.5 strikes the same note: "Behold, I was brought forth in iniquity, and in sin did my mother conceive me." We find similar pessimistic echoes in Ps. cxliii.2 and cxxx.3, while in Ps. xc physical decay and moral guilt are again quite plainly linked. In connection with Prov. xx.9: "Who can say, 'I have made my heart clean, I am pure from my sin,' " Ben-Sirach acknowledges that "we all deserve punishment." (viii.5.) He associates the physical condition of man with his moral imperfection. (xxii.29-32; cf. Job xiv.17-20; xxv.2-6.) These descriptions of the human condition, however, never mention the fall in paradise. It is as though they have come into being independent of Genesis, and wish to state in their own way what the story of paradise wished to say.

But the Old Testament believer continues to appreciate the body as a created good. He knows no dualism in which a good part of man contrasts with an evil part. Neither does St. Paul acknowledge such a dualism, because the same man, seen as a totality, is the subject both of sinful desire and of Christian love. Our members can be lent to both uses. In itself bodiliness, together with sexuality, is a natural good. True that man is an uncompleted creature, and that in addition he has not answered to the purposes of a Creator calling him to perfection, so that he has delivered the world to the power of evil. But it remains certain that creation, as we know it within and without, is good. Modern man is on the way to assimilating this insight and guards himself against the depreciation of certain aspects of bodiliness. To the extent that this takes place in abstraction from God and faith, the insight holds a great danger, because man can control creation only through God.

The longing for God which lives in the depths of man is

the sounding-board of God's creative revelation. God made himself a road to the heart of man in the calling of Abraham and of the Chosen People, though all this is the prelude to his work of salvation through Christ. When the time is fulfilled, and the Son of God is to appear on earth as man, he will be conceived by a Virgin, in whom Israel's desire for salvation has become a pure receptivity.

# 8

# THE MOTHER OF GOD

Although Holy Scripture does not tell us much about Mary, we find one clear foundation-stone for the article of faith "conceived by the Holy Ghost, born of the Virgin Mary." The Creed is speaking of Christ, and at the same time refers to Mary. Since we are going to discuss Mary in the light of evolution, we limit ourselves to the conception of the Son of God in the womb of the Virgin Mary through the overshadowing of the Spirit of the Most High.

The advance of God's creative work is marked, in Scripture, by three primary occurrences: the creation of the ordered universe, the creation of the earthly man, and the creation of the heavenly man. In the Bible the first two creations follow closely upon one another, because the evolutionary image was unknown. The three creative acts of God display a striking mutual resemblance:

Gen. i.2-5: "The earth was without form and void, and darkness was upon the face of the deep; and the *Spirit of God* was moving over the face of the waters. And God said,

'Let there be light'; and there was light. And God saw that the light was good; and God separated the light from the darkness. God *called the light Day,* and the darkness he called Night. And there was evening and there was morning, one day."

Gen. ii.7: "Then the *Lord God* formed man of dust from the ground, and breathed into his nostrils the breath of life; and man became a living being."

Luke i.35,38: "The *Holy Spirit* will come upon you, and the power of the *Most High* will overshadow you; therefore the child to be born will be called *holy, the Son of God. . . .* And Mary said, 'Behold, I am the handmaid of the Lord; let it be to me according to your word.' "

What existed before the creation of light had no order and was not knowable. These two aspects of the primitive mass are, it is true, divided as land and sea, but just as land and primitive water together form the primitive mass, so formlessness and darkness make up *one* qualification: they are the concrete description of nothing. The purpose of this description becomes clear from the creation of light. As we have already noted in a previous chapter, the writer is undoubtedly thinking here of Wisdom, which in the Old Testament theology of creation is the ordering creative power of God, called in Wisd. of Sol. vii.25-6: "a pure emanation of the glory of the Almighty . . . a reflection of eternal light." When God creates he sees his wisdom in creation. Through Wisdom the universe arrives at orderly being, and is raised by the light of Wisdom from darkness to knowability. That is the first indwelling of the creation by Wisdom.

Now what meaning has the Spirit of God which moves above the waters? Before we answer this question we must consult what Scripture says elsewhere about the Spirit of Yahweh. In the chapter on creative revelation, we saw that the Hebrews made no distinction between the existence of the creature as such and the orientation to God present in the creature. Thus human intelligence is essentially directedness to God. If it is not directed to God, then it is darkness, and of no account. It annuls itself. Now, *this orientation to God comes from the Spirit of God*. Seen from God's side, *the Spirit is the creative gaze by which God sees the creature*. The parallelism between the Spirit and the Face or Presence of God is striking:

> Create in me a clean heart, O God,
> and put a new and right spirit within me.
> Cast me not away from thy presence,
> and take not thy holy Spirit from me.
>
> [Ps. li.10-11]

The two verses are saying precisely the same thing, only *v.* 10 sets out from man and *v.* 11 from God. A clean heart is equivalent in the Bible to a just opinion or a good intention. Here the directedness is expressed which in *v.* 10b is called a right spirit. The *reciprocal relation* between God and man occurs through the Spirit.

Hence other aspects become clear which must be brought into connection with the Holy Spirit. Because the orientation of man to God implies obedience to God's will, the Spirit of Yahweh is seen as that which inspires man to fulfil his commands. "A new heart I will give you; and I will take out of your flesh the heart of stone and give you a heart of flesh. And I will put my spirit within you, and cause you to walk in my statutes and be careful to observe my ordinances. You shall dwell in the land which I gave to your fathers; and you shall be my people, and I will be your God. And I will deliver you from all your uncleannesses." (Ezek. xxxvi.26-9.) We have to place the word "holy," which so often accompanies the word "Spirit," in this context: where the Spirit comes, there sin vanishes.

Since obedience to the will of God means letting the creative will of God realize its purpose, the Spirit is called "a spirit of life" (Rom. viii.2); or the Spirit of the living God; the Spirit which gives life (2 Cor. iii.3, 6).

The vivifying power of God's Spirit operates not only in man but in all living beings:

> When thou hidest thy *face,* they are dismayed;
> when thou takest away their *breath* [life-spirit], they die
> and return to their dust.
> When thou sendest forth thy *Spirit* they are created,
> and thou renewest the *face* of the earth.
>
> [Ps. civ.24-30]

In these verses both the parallelism of face and spirit and the life-creating power of the Spirit of God are prominent. We can put it like this: When God turns his face towards the earth, earth also receives a face, or receives sight. God does this by sending forth his Spirit. The word "earth" in *v.* 30 we must take to indicate the surface of the earth which is to be renewed. But there is a "face" of the earth and of the whole universe, which is less skin-deep, and that is what Gen. i-2 has to do with. It is the intelligibility of the creation as such.

Without a face the universe is chaos and darkness. Properly speaking, it is nothing. Above, we called Wisdom the light which drives away the darkness and produces order out of chaos. Wisdom bestows a "face" upon the universe. The two aspects are united if we say that by his Spirit God gives a face to the universe, and that Wisdom *is* the face of the universe. This relationship of Spirit and Wisdom is also applicable to the relation of God to man, especially as we find this in the New Testament. When we confine ourselves to the creation of the ordered universe according to Gen. i.2-3, we see that God lets his Spirit blow over the unordered dark chaos and gives it a face by the fertilizing action of the Spirit. Its face is the indwelling Wisdom. The universe is conceived by the Spirit of God. Wisdom "is made universe," just as later it will become man. The wisdom of God appears in the figure of Jesus of Nazareth.

But in between there lies the creation of man. "Then the Lord God formed man of dust from the ground, and breathed into his nostrils the breath of life; and man became a living being." The breath of life comes out of the mouth of God and makes man alive. The stuff of the earth receives a face; it is man! Man is created after God's image and likeness, as the writer of Gen. i puts it. Man is the image of God, though it be at an infinite distance. The wisdom of God dwells in him, the Wisdom which John called the Logos which is the light of the world. The Light of the World, previously "become universe," breaks through here into human intelligence, not in any pantheistic sense, but through created participation in the divine Wisdom.

This event has a reflexive effect upon the whole of creation. The man who resembles God, who is orientated to God, and who arose from the earth, populates the world and subdues it. He has dominion over the fishes of the sea, the birds of the air, and all living creatures that move upon the earth. This dominion is indicated in Gen. ii.19-20 in the giving of names: "So out of the ground the Lord God formed every beast of the field and every bird of the air, and brought them to the man to see what he would call them; and whatever the man called every living creature, that was its name. The man gave names to all cattle, and to the birds of the air, and to every beast of the field; but for the man there was not found a helper fit for him." The giving of names expresses dominion, but, as in Gen. i, so here this dominion must not be understood in our usual sense, any more than it is thinkable that, in the usual sense, man can be said to rule over the fishes and the birds. Man then *knows* the creation, and in that lies his dominion. If one knows something, one can name it. But when he looks around he sees no single eye from which the human spirit radiates.

At the creation of man the living breath of God was breathed out afresh. Wisdom has now become man—in another sense, certainly, than the later one, yet in a very real sense. The wisdom of God here expresses itself in the light of that reason which unveils all creatures before the gaze of man, so that he can name them. We know nowadays that God did not breathe the breath of life, which makes a man, into dust, but into an animated being. Yet this makes little difference, because all creatures beneath man are the preparatory work of God, which he allows to fall back into the dust. But man stands higher than all these, because he is created as receptivity to God, turned to him with a veiled vision; veiled, because he knows God only from his works, to which he gives a name.

Luke i.35, 38: "The Holy Spirit will come upon you, and the power of the Most High will overshadow you; therefore the child to be born will be called holy, the Son of God . . . And Mary said, 'Behold, I am the handmaid of the Lord; let it be to me according to your word.' "

The Church, in its sense of faith, has always seen more in the relationship of Mary to Jesus than ordinary human motherhood. It shows the dignity and sanctity of Jesus pouring back upon his mother. Thus the motherhood of

Mary must be seen as grounding and comprehending all the privileges ascribed to her by tradition. Mary conceived the Son of God in her womb without the intervention of a man. In this way her virginity becomes a receptivity focused wholly on God, and it is precisely by way of this directedness to God that Mary conceives by the Holy Ghost. On the feast of the Motherhood of Mary, instituted in 1931 by Pope Pius XI in memory of the Council of Ephesus, which, 1500 years before, had solemnly proclaimed the title of Theotokos, the Mother of God, priests and religious read in the Breviary the words of Leo the Great: ". . . a royal virgin, chosen from the house of David, so that she, who was to bear a holy fruit, should conceive her divine child *rather in her heart than in her body*."

In these words of the great Pope the whole of Mariology is contained in germ. Let us first pause at the datum that Mary is a child of Israel. Then we shall go back still further to the Patriarchs and beyond. We then arrive at the remarkable history of mankind whereby the Bible bridges the gap between the first man and Abraham. In it we find the accent upon the power of evil in the world: the first son of Adam is a fratricide. Then we read that God destroys sinful humanity by the Flood. Hardly has this story ended than we see the inhabitants of the whole earth challenging God by building a city with a tower reaching to heaven. God renders the plan vain by the confusion of tongues. This time he scatters mankind without destroying it. Then Abraham appears on the scene.

In all these stories, just as in the paradise story, we are properly concerned with man wandering lost on the earth, but not forsaken by God. Evil is always turned aside by the faithfulness of God, and from the very beginning God has those who serve him. But this becomes historically comprehensible only from the time of the Patriarchs, and achieves a clearly defined form in the Israel of prophetic times. Israel is the place where the revelation of God's salvation irrupts into the world. The People of Yahweh knows itself to be privileged above all nations. It is chosen from the inhabitants of the earth to render God the worship due to him: "Now, therefore, if you will obey my voice and keep my covenant, you shall be my own possession among all peoples; for all the earth is mine, and you shall be to me a kingdom of priests and a holy nation." (Exod. xix.5-6.) This is the role of Israel, in the name of all creation, in the name of all other peoples, and in the name of the heavens and the earth and all that they contain.

Praise the Lord from the earth,
you sea-monsters and all deeps,
fire and hail, snow and frost,
stormy wind fulfilling his command!
Mountains and all hills,
fruit trees and all cedars!
Beasts and all cattle,
creeping things and flying birds!
Kings of the earth and all peoples,
princes and all rulers of the earth!

Young men and maidens together,
old men and children.

[Ps. cxlviii.7-12]

In the disasters which strike the People of God, first through the fall of the Northern Kingdom and then through the fall of Judah, the Prophets speak of a new time of salvation which will dawn for Israel in the future. In the expectation of this salvation Israel sees itself as at once the representative of all nations and of all creation. Through Israel all peoples will learn to know the will of God and the world will possess the peace of paradise.

It shall come to pass in the latter days
that the mountain of the house of the Lord
shall be established as the highest of the mountains,
and shall be raised above the hills;
and all the nations shall flow to it,
and many peoples shall come, and say:
"Come let us go up to the mountain of the Lord,
to the house of the God of Jacob;
that he may teach us his ways
and that we may walk in his paths."
For out of Zion shall go forth the law,
and the word of the Lord from Jerusalem.
The wolf shall dwell with the lamb,
and the leopard shall lie down with the kid,
and the calf and the lion and the fatling together,
and a little child shall lead them.

> The cow and the bear shall feed;
> their young shall lie down together;
> and the lion shall eat straw like the ox.
> The sucking child shall play over the hole of the asp,
> and the weaned child shall put his hand on the adder's den.
>
> [Isa. ii.2-3; xi.6-8]

Thus did Israel expect for centuries the realization of the coming salvation that God would prepare for all peoples as a light which would shine upon the Gentiles, and as the glory of the people of Israel. (Luke ii.31-2.) In this way the distance becomes more apparent between Israel as a nation possessing political dominion and the holy Remnant, which represents the true Israel. The true Israel consists of the hidden ones in the land; these are the true bearers of God's promises. Mary is one of these. She received the divine Wisdom rather in her heart than in her body. The last point is of decisive significance if we are to give, in exact perspective, the exceptional place of Mary in God's creation.

What takes place in her is nothing less than the personal union of the divine Wisdom with the creature. Wisdom had already come down to creation when God called the universe into existence. Then Wisdom gave herself to the human intelligence directed to God. Now this directedness to God is to take the form of the personal turning of the Son to the Father, in the form of a man. This is the salvation by which all redeemed life will live to eternity. The incarnation of Wisdom in substantial union with the creature heralds the last phase of evolution. The earthly man gives way to the heavenly. That this is not visible in the appearance of Jesus on earth is the consequence of his hiding his glory under the veil of his earthly body; it takes nothing away from the actuality of the occurrence. The incarnation of Wisdom in the womb of Mary is in principle the end of the old world and the beginning of the new. It is a unique act of the creation of God, who sends his Spirit at this point to give creation a new face, the face of Jesus Christ, on which the glory of God shines. (2 Cor. iv.6.)

At the creation of the first man God evoked from the dust of the earth, already made ready by a long evolution, a partner to a dialogue, who by nature was orientated to the knowledge of his Creator. The first man, and every man after him, is in his nature a quest of God, but in spite of this high dignity he is also dust of the earth. "Just as we have borne the image of the man of dust, we shall also bear the image of the man of heaven." (1 Cor. xv.48.) At the creation of every man the creation of the first man is re-enacted, out of the earth hitherto prepared. The poet of Ps. cxxxix interprets this thought when he identifies the maternal womb with the "depths of the earth." (*vv.* 13-15.)

For thou didst form my inward parts,
thou didst knit me together in my mother's womb,
I praise thee, for thou art fearful and wonderful.
Wonderful are thy works!
Thou knowest me right well;

my frame was not hidden from thee,
when I was being made in secret,
intricately wrought in the depths of the earth.

The incarnation of the Son of God introduces a new phase of evolution. In him the earthly man becomes a heavenly man. Just as with the creation of the earthly man, so with the creation of the heavenly man; it is preceded by a long preparation, which now advances not on the biological but on the personal level. Now that the heavenly man is to be created, God regards man's longing for salvation. In the heart of Mary the longing of Israel is expressed, and through Israel the longing of all nations, and through all nations the longing of creation to be freed from the slavery of corruption. Man who in the beginning was created as openness to God, and in the revelation to Israel learned by falling and rising to live out this openness, comes in Mary to stand before God as unspoiled receptivity to grace, to a salvation destined for all peoples which shall blossom in a new heaven and a new earth.

Out of the words of Leo the Great which we quoted above speaks the tradition of the Church, which has always connected the events of the Incarnation with a personal encounter between God and Mary. We do not understand the Incarnation properly if, in the manner of the Nestorians, we detach Christ from the Son of God, and separate the body of Mary from her spirit. The Incarnation has also a bodily side, expressed in the conception by a virgin, but herein it possesses primarily a personal aspect, which, on Mary's side, consists in her turning to God, and on God's side in the sending out of his Spirit. These two aspects should not be separated. Mary gave not only her body but her heart. As human, and turned to God in pure receptivity, she is the earth out of which God raises the heavenly man by his Spirit. By the intervention of the Holy Spirit he prepared the body and the soul of the Virgin and Mother to be a worthy lodging for his Son. These are the words in which the Church interprets a centuries-old tradition in the prayer after the antiphon, *Salve Regina*.

The earth from which the heavenly man is formed is not only matter but also spirit: the spirit of the Holy Virgin directed to God. As I said, this earth is a human being turned to God in unspotted receptivity. By this I do not, of course, mean to say that the soul of Christ was formed of the soul of Mary. Yet if we reject such a suggestion, it still does not follow that Mary is only a biological substratum for the Incarnation. Mary's longing for salvation and her willingness to serve are part of the preparation for the creation of the heavenly man, just as at a lower level pre-human forms of life prepared the coming of the man of earth. But the heavenly man himself is an irreducible creation of God, just as the earthly man was. In both instances the preparatory stage nearest to the new creation—that is, which comes closest to the new phase of evolution—has its irreplaceable meaning. The longing for salvation and the willingness to serve which characterize Mary have their own place in God's creative work. Whoever wants to view the Incarnation as the birth of the Son of God from a sinful mother, and eventually to involve a human father, is compelled to see in Jesus a purely earthly man, or to split up the God-Man like a Nestorian. Then no new phase is ushered in, and the man of the future will be no different from the man of the present.

The dogma of the Immaculate Conception, as worded in the solemn declaration of 8 December 1854, says that Mary, from the first moment of her conception in the womb of her mother, was warranted free, by a special grace and privilege of Almighty God, from every stain which flows from the sinful deed in the beginning. To this it adds that this conception has its source in the future merits of Jesus Christ, the saviour of the human race.

In line with what we said in Chapter 3 about original sin we may here also cast our eye towards the future rather than the past. What is at issue here is not only a warrant against the influence exerted by sinful humanity upon every new person but, in addition, an unsullied openness to the future. Mary was created to be the mother of God's Son. That is why she is already drawn by anticipation into the sphere of the creative and redemptive incarnation of the Son of God. Because God, in his Son made man, wishes to complete man, and, through man, the world, he has from the beginning looked down mercifully upon man, and for centuries evoked the longing of Israel for salvation. The divine Wisdom was already present in creation and enlightened the Prophets and the godly persons of the Old Covenant. In Mary this preparation reaches its peak. Her immaculate conception takes the form of an immaculate receptivity. While it is true that all other human beings are created as openness to God, even in the Christian dispensation they can actualize this capacity only by falling and rising, until in the next life they can truly stand open to God; Mary was created by God in pure receptivity, to conceive by the Holy Spirit and to become the mother of the Son of God.

When we reflected on these things, we were reminded of the phrase by which Mary revealed herself to the girl, Bernadette: "I *am* the Immaculate Conception." Should we be right to hear in these words the active sense of "immaculate conception"? No theologian spoke or speaks in this way. Theology recognizes the immaculate conception *of* Mary, and interprets it in a passive sense. It is striking, too, that Mary did not reveal herself to Bernadette on the feast of her immaculate conception, but on the 25th of March, the day on which the Church remembers that the Son of God was conceived in the womb of Mary.

To the theologian it may seem like a profanation to enquire about the place of Mary in evolution. This revulsion, let me say once again, is a symptom of a closed theology, which can no longer find its way to the reality of the cosmos as it shows itself to us with the aid of the sciences. The place of Mary in evolution reveals in a new way how great she is as a person. The creative work of God achieves a breakthrough at a decisive point only by means of the consenting receptivity of Mary. Each of us must allow the creative work of God to be completed in the whole of his life, through faith and through love in which faith works. The old man in us must make way for the new man which we shall be, but only by our own consent. In Mary the old *world* is called to arise to its completion in a new *world*. She is the voice of the universe looking forward to completion. Bernard of Clairvaux expresses this splendidly in his second sermon for Pentecost: "With justice are the eyes of all creation bent upon you, for in you and through you and out of you the loving hand of the Most High has newly created everything that he created."

Does all this square with the modest place occupied by Mary in the Gospels? Why not? The great Acts of God are consummated inconspicuously. We should do wrong to attribute to Mary a kind of omniscience or any striking activity. Her greatness lies singly and solely in her pure receptivity. She is not in competition with the sovereignty of God but is the person who acknowledged this sovereignty in the most radical fashion. She is the greatest of the faithful, always wondering about her Son, and following him to the foot of the cross.

# 9

# THE LITURGY OF JESUS

In the New Testament Christ is a particular person, but we notice that afterwards this person, in a mysterious way, represents a collectivity. The faithful share his death and resurrection with him and in him. He lives in the faithful. He abides in them and they in him. Jews and Gentiles are transformed in him into one new man. In short, Christ's work of salvation is not something confined to his own person but touches all men in a mysterious way. As an individual, Christ represents all men.

The background of this way of looking at things could, I argued, be shown by means of the "progressive incarnation" described in the previous chapter and elsewhere in the book. In the beginning of creation Wisdom becomes the universe. Wisdom is in everything as the ordaining creative power of God, and creation in its manysidedness shows forth the manysided wisdom of God which manifests itself in creation. Here the first movement of concentration takes place insofar as man, created as God's image, has dominion over all other creatures, on condition that he looks to God. Given that man cannot live out this orientation to God by his own powers, the revelation of God intervenes in the history of man, taking concrete shape in Israel: "Then the Creator of all things gave me a commandment, and the one who created me assigned a place for my tent. And he said, 'Make your dwelling in Jacob, and in Israel receive your inheritance.'" (Ecclus. xxiv.8.) The indwelling of Wisdom in Israel does not consist only in the formulation of the Law and the prophecies by the people. The true revelation consummates itself in the heart of the people; among all the nations it is Israel that knows what pleases Yahweh. That is the second concentration: Israel becomes the light of the world. That Wisdom which carries the creation and makes of man the lord of creation establishes its dominion in Jerusalem. (Ecclus. xxiv.11.) Israel is the representative of the nations and of creation when she stands before Yahweh in the Temple. That Wisdom, which is in creation and in the nations, praises the Creator through Israel.

The last concentration occurs when Wisdom reveals itself in one man. This concentration is already prefigured in the one sanctuary where Israel celebrates her liturgy, and in Yahweh's abiding there. Jesus is the new temple (John ii.21-2), and celebrates a new liturgy. He is the representative of Israel, and through Israel of all humanity, and through humanity of all creation. Wisdom, which by her creative power carries the universe, the nations and Israel, is revealed as a person in Jesus of Nazareth. Jesus of Nazareth declares himself as the Servant of Yahweh (Isa. xl-lvi) and as the Son of Man (Dan. vii). Of both figures it is hard to say whether they must be understood as a person or as a collectivity. They are both.

This approach to the person of Jesus of Nazareth gives some insight into the reason why, in Col. i and Heb. ii-iii, a cosmic extension is attributed to the work of salvation, in which there is a reference back to the mediation of Wisdom in the creation of all things. We then understand better how incarnate Wisdom can represent all men. It is because she, who is revealed in the person of Jesus, lives in all men through the light of reason. The liturgy which Jesus offers to God by the sacrifice of the cross, and the heavenly and eternal praise which follows from it, is offered in the name of all men and of all creation.

In the New Testament Christ's work of salvation is spoken of in divers ways. Instead of making our own synthesis of all these, let us use the New Testament meditation on this work which is so splendidly presented to us in the Letter to the Hebrews.

The purpose of the letter is to confirm wavering Christians in the Faith. From the text there is no more to be said about the identity of these Christians than that they were undoubtedly converted Jews who, exposed to persecution by their fellow Jews, showed a tendency to return to the Jewish religion. This connects with the fact that the writer contrasts Christ with the various mediators of the Old Covenant: prophets, angels, Moses, Joshua, and above all the Levitical high priest. It is his intention to show that Christ excels all these in dignity. The Old Covenant is terminated; Christ is the high priest and mediator of a New Covenant. Here the accent falls upon the celestial figure of the high priest. The sacrifice of the cross is the fountain of salvation, but salvation is incorporated in the eternal life of the heavenly mediator, who as the liturgist of the sanctuary of heaven is seated at the right hand of God. The heavenly high priest overshadows the priesthood of the Old Testament.

The current theology saw the priesthood of Jesus almost exclusively in terms of the sacrifice of the cross, while his heavenly priesthood went comparatively unattended to. But just as we cannot separate the death of Jesus from his resurrection, so we cannot separate the earthly phase of his priestly service from the heavenly liturgy which the glorified Christ consummates. The connection between them is established already in i.3: "When he had made purification for sins, he sat down at the right hand of the Majesty on high."

Likewise the priesthood of Jesus comes under discussion in ii.17-18, to be picked up again in iv.14-16. After that the author expands the theme, although he once more interrupts his exposition by an exhortation, which runs from v.11 to the end of Chapter 6, where he again arrives at his subject. He now develops without interruption his conception of the sacrifice and the priesthood of the New Covenant: vii.1-x.18. In the exposition given here we shall not delay over every detail of the text but try, by the aid of the most important passages, to give an impression of the teaching about Christ's earthly and heavenly liturgy.

In viii.6-13 Christ is called the mediator of a covenant more perfect than the old. The proof of this is given in ix.1-14, followed by the conclusion: Therefore he is the mediator of a new covenant. The proof consists in this, that the liturgical service of Jesus surpasses the Levitical one in many respects. The benefits of salvation, which Christ obtains by his sacrifice, thus far excel those which are attained by the old service of the Temple. Let us look more closely at the passage (ix.1-14).

In ix.1-10 a short sketch is given of the institution of the Levitical sanctuary and of the ritual duties there performed. The sanctuary was divided into two, and the passage from one to the other was through a curtain. The front division, the Holy Place, was daily entered by the priests, who there performed various liturgical functions. Behind the second curtain was the Holy of Holies, accessible only to the high priest, and then only once a year, namely on the great Day of Atonement.

The function of the high priest on the Day of Atonement is the main matter of comparison. The sacrificial service of Christ is described in ix.11-12 on the analogy of this rite of atonement. The incompleteness of this rite is declared to us in ix.7-8: "Into the second only the high priest goes, and he but once a year, and not without taking blood which he offers for himself and for the errors of the people. By this the Holy Spirit indicates that the way into the sanctuary is not yet opened as long as the outer tent is still standing."

On the Day of Atonement the sacrificial animals were slaughtered outside the sanctuary. Then the high priest took the blood, and went with it into the Holy of Holies to sprinkle it upon the covering of the Tabernacle. The Holy of Holies was the place where Yahweh dwelt amidst his people. Thus the high priest, who trod this place, found himself *in the presence of Yahweh.*

Hence the thought of the author is this, that the presence of Yahweh in the old worship is really *not* accessible. Once a year, and not without the blood offering, the high priest went up to Yahweh. Offering which one makes annually does not seem to be very efficacious; otherwise the offering would have ceased long ago (x.1-4). By instituting the old Temple service the Holy Spirit wished to indicate that the way to the sanctuary, understood as the place where God dwells, was not open while the Levitical temple still served. God was not yet accessible.

After that, in ix.11-12, the sacrifice of Christ is described. The sublimity of Christ's oblation appears from many circumstances. He enters a sanctuary which does not belong to this creation. Elsewhere, this sanctuary is called heaven, not the heaven which overarches the earth, but heaven regarded as the presence of God. Christ enters this sanctuary with his own blood, not, like the Levitical high priest, "with blood not his own" (ix.25). Christ enters the sanctuary once and for all; one sacrifice was sufficient, since he could effect an eternal salvation through it. For good measure, we add that Christ enters the sanctuary to *stay* there. The high priest offers and then returns, but Christ remains in the sanctuary as the *eternal high priest:* "We have such a high priest, one who is seated at the right hand of the throne of the Majesty in heaven, a minister in the sanctuary and the true tent which is set up not by man but by the Lord" (viii.1-2).

To get a good conception of Christ's high-priestly function we must go more deeply into this "sacrificial procession" which commences on earth, and proceeds by way of the cross and the glorification to the seat at the right hand of God. Cross, resurrection, and ascension are included in this sacrificial way. They form one single action. Christ returns offering from earth to heaven, from which he went forth in the Incarnation. To use the words of St. John's Gospel: The Son of Man ascends to where he was before (vi.62); he came from God and was going to God (xiii.3), or as Jesus repeatedly says: "I go to the Father." Jesus departs from earth as mortal man and is with the Father in glory.

The description of Christ's sacrificial way in Hebrews proceeds on the assumption that Christ on earth is outside heaven. He is not with God. His liturgy is an approach to God. Just as the Levitical high priest enters the Holy of Holies from outside, so Jesus with his own blood enters the heavenly sanctuary to appear before God.

As set out in v.1-4, a high priest must belong to the

community which he represents by his function of mediator. He must know what man is, and what goes on in man. Only a high priest who is one of the people possesses the qualifications necessary for the fulfilling of the function. Christ satisfies these requirements, "for we have not a high priest who is unable to sympathise with our weaknesses, but one who in every respect has been tempted as we are, yet without sinning" (Heb. iv.15). Hence he had to become equal to his brothers in all things to bring their interests before God as a compassionate and faithful high priest, and to give satisfaction for the sins of the people. The suffering by which he is himself tried enables him to bring help to all who are tried. (ii.17-18.)

The trials connect with the fact that Jesus is outside heaven, and outside the presence of God. The trials stand in the sign of his solidarity with man on earth. Jesus is tempted as we are, and here the reference is primarily to Christians persecuted on account of their faith. Because Jesus has stood firm in these temptations without sinning, he can now help all those who have to travel to God by the same road. Jesus is "the forerunner" (vi.20). He has pioneered the way from earth to God. (x.19-20.)

What would have happened if Jesus had not opened the way? Man would never have reached God. Men would have continued to wander on this earth, driven this way and that by an insatiable urge for life. Death would continue to be suspended over their lives as a threat which could not be outflanked. "Since therefore the children share in flesh and blood, he himself likewise partook of the same nature, that through death he might destroy him who has the power of death, that is, the devil, and deliver all those who through fear of death were subject to lifelong bondage." (ii.14-15.)

The coming into this world of the Son of God, the going out from the Father, consists in a coming in an earthly condition, biblically indicated by "flesh and blood." This earthly condition is threatened by death, because man is in no state to do the will of God. Where the will of God is not done, the way to life is barred. Man becomes the slave of sin and of the devil and brings down death upon his head.

The incarnation of the Son of God means that a man has arisen who *is* able to do the will of God. Upon his entrance into the world he says, "I have come to do thy will, O God." (x.5-10.) Jesus consummates the will of God in that very existence of flesh and blood which belongs to us. That which other men are in no condition to do is here fulfilled "by the power of an indestructible life" (vii.16). The Son of God himself stands behind human existence, which through him turns aside the power of sin, and breaks through the ramparts of death. Here is a man who achieves what every human heart desires without having the proper power to obtain it. But Jesus is not just an individual who finds the way to God, but above all this is bound to the generation of men, whom he represents in his liturgy. He overcomes the sin which has got human existence into its clutches. He wrestles with the death which already dwells in the hearts of men. He has come "in the likeness of sinful flesh" (Rom. viii.3) and has a solidarity with sinning humanity. In his incarnation the Son of God came to stand at the side of men, outside of heaven and at a distance from God, both on account of the earthly condition "which cannot inherit the kingdom of God" (1 Cor. xv.50) and of the sinful world in which he lives.

On the one hand Jesus is one with sinful humanity condemned to death, and on the other, he is obedient to the will of God. The combination of the two aspects marks him as the high priest who brings his sacrifice. The sacrifice consists in faithfulness to the divine commission to die, a faithfulness which reaches its climax precisely when Jesus is most fully united with the situation of man in exile, that is, in his suffering and death.

Though the will of Jesus was steadfastly directed to God, he yet had real inner struggles. This is clear to us from the account of the Passion in the Gospels. Our letter, too, speaks very realistically about this in v.7. There, there is mention of loud cries and tears, of prayers and supplications, which Jesus directs to God, who can save him from death. The continuation of this text tells us a great deal if we wish to understand what happened in Christ's suffering. In v. 7 it says literally that Jesus prayed to God to save him from death, and then that he is heard on account of his obedience. But was Jesus heard? In fact he suffered death! When we put this question, we have too limited a comprehension of the concept of death. We think of the fact of dying. The writer is thinking of the death which Jesus shares with men, and which can be overcome only by obedience and life in God. When Jesus asks to be rescued he is, through his solidarity with men, placed in a certain relation to death from which he prays to be freed.

That prayer is answered—a point which is worked out in *vv.* 8-10: "and he was heard for his godly fear. Although he was a son, he learned obedience through what he suffered; and being made perfect he became the source of eternal salvation to all who obey him, being designated by God a high priest after the order of Melchizedek." The answering of the prayer for liberation from death consists in the glorification. But the road to this glorification runs over obedience through the midst of trials and death. This obedience, too, is the fruit of prayer. Obedience is always in direct opposition to death, which has its deepest centre in disobedience, the turning-away from God. That is why the extreme of obedience is suffering, and death itself the victory over death and suffering, the definitive overcoming of the situation which man has got into by the contributory action of the devil. That is why Jesus, in his suffering and death, "is made perfect." His adherence to the will of God is tried to the utmost and shows itself inflexible, and this inflexible subjection to God receives the crown of eternal life; for obedience is always the deepest centre of life. The eternal life of Jesus in his glorification with God is the fully human manifestation of his inflexible subjection to the will of God. Then, far from ending at death, this subjection of the Son to the Father, this attitude of obedience to the will of God, is eternally confirmed in his glorified life. On the grounds of this eternal subjection to the Father, Jesus is called by God to be a high priest forever after the order of Melchizedek. We see that the heavenly liturgy of Jesus is born out of the earthly and is its glorified continuation. The attitude of submission to the will of the Father is the connecting link.

The author fixes our attention on heaven rather than on the cross. According to him it is only in his glorification that Jesus reaches the final form of his function as high priest. In this letter, the appointment of Jesus to be high priest is usually placed in the moment of glorification. This way of looking at things runs wholly parallel with that of some of the texts of the New Testament where only in his glorification does Jesus fully possess his titles of Messiah, Son, and Lord. (Acts ii.36; Rom. i.4; Phil. i.9-11; Heb. i.4-5.) Not that Jesus did not possess these titles before; but only in his glorification do they attain their full scope. The earthly life of Jesus is a phase of transition, in which the veil of transience hides his true being.

This great emphasis upon the heavenly priesthood of Jesus may seem somewhat strange to us. We should then reflect that we do not do full justice to the eschatological angle of the redemptive action of God in Christ. The final form of salvation is achieved only at the end of time. Only then will the New Covenant be fully realized. It is not true that the sacrifice of Jesus is a passing action by which salvation is merited, and that after this the high-priestly function of Jesus fades out into something which it is theologically difficult to define as a celebration of God. The contrary is true: the heavenly liturgy is the permanent and eternal content of the high priesthood of Jesus, in which the sacrifice of the cross is certainly a decisive, but is at the same time an introductory, phase. By the blood of his cross Jesus builds a road to the presence of God, whom in eternity he honours with his subjection. This subjection is the obedience of the Covenant, in a manner proper to the New Covenant. In the power of Jesus' obedience the faithful on earth are called back from their "dead works" and orientated to the *latria,* the celebration of the living God (ix.14), which they shall celebrate with the heavenly liturgist in the final completion of the New and Eternal Covenant.

We should underestimate the significance of the theology of this letter were we to hold that it had to do only with the reconciliation of man and the world. It is true that the moral categories play a decisive role here, as appears from the use of notions such as obedience, the will of God, and others, but these moral categories imply here, as everywhere else and always in the Bible, the creative action of God. In Christ, the man of "flesh and blood" (ii.14) is called to an eternal life beyond the world. The presence of God is not accessible to flesh and blood. For that another manner of existence is necessary, a new creation.

This perspective is opened to us in the first two chapters, where the cosmic dimension of salvation becomes clear.

There is a present world and a future world. (ii.5.) The Son, who in i.3 is described in the same terms previously applied to Wisdom, is, as First-born, born anew into the world. (i.6.) Just as Wisdom stood at the beginning of God's creative work, so Christ stands at the beginning of the world to come, the true nature of which is not yet unveiled for us: "We do not yet see everything in subjection to him." (ii.8.) When once we see the redemptive work of Christ as a work of creation, the possibility lies open of saying something, from the standpoint of the mystery of Christ, about the meaning of suffering in the evolutionary image of the world. It is clear that, according to Hebrews, trials have a significance for man in his growth towards completion. Christ bestowed this significance. By his suffering and death the universe passes into a new and last phase of its existence.

# 10

# THE MEANING OF SUFFERING

If we regard human suffering down the course of time, and the sufferings of human beings individually, from the point of view of their external form, we cannot deny a continuity with the cosmic and animal stages of the earth. Earthquakes, hurricanes, climatic disasters and other threats from nature are still factors which make the existence of man and animal unsafe. Right before us is the fact that animals devour each other. The human situation is possibly even worse, because man destroys his own kind. An imaginary observer of our planet would be most astonished to see that beings endowed with reason, and capable of reflection, choose to obliterate each other on a national scale with the technical productions of that very reason. But in more restricted social groupings too—family, village, city—people all too often confront one another with hate in their eyes. Is it not perhaps true that hate belongs to the basic structure of human nature? We can answer Yes, but with the restriction that we are speaking about men who do not accept their life from God but trust in their own strength. It must be added that the man who does not live by God is false to his human essence, and in this sense continues, as it were, the animal level of existence. Then the meaning which, in God's dispensation, attaches to human suffering must disappear.

Human suffering is something quite different from animal suffering. Looked at from the outside this is not apparent, because, biologically speaking, we observe the same phenomena of physical destruction, and in the higher animals evidence even of psychological emotions which remind us of man's. In this context, philosophy talks about shadows of existence.[1] This superficial resemblance should not blind us to the fundamental difference between man and animal. Man is a rational being, and by virtue of his rational nature he experiences pain, and other onslaughts upon his integrity, quite differently from the animal. In comparison with human pain the suffering of an animal can hardly be called pain. The experience of an animal that is hurt is inaccessible to man because it is essentially different from our own, and is on a decisively lower plane. That is why man is free to hurt animals where it is necessary for human welfare. But he is forbidden to torture animals, because he is then expressing his own evil through the animal.

Thus human suffering is not a direct continuation of what has happened and is happening on lower levels in the cosmos.

[1] In existentialist philosophy, *Existenz*=*human* existence. Tr.

We can say with complete justice that before man existed pain was not felt on earth. Before that time there was no sorrow; no being ever hated another, and no being ever felt cut off. All this appeared on earth only with man, and man, who experiences these things, is called upon to find a meaning for suffering. In the process, suffering acquires a positive value, so that finally what the Bible says really is true: "And God saw everything that he had made, and behold, it was very good." (Gen. i.31.) But this can only be comprehended by one who has faith.

In our explanation of original sin we have already noted that man is an ambiguous being, because biologically he is related to the animal, and, as a person, to God. The earthly man is on the road to union with God. This "ambiguousness" is not a dualism but a commission to self-realization. Seen biologically, the human body is very closely related to that of the most developed animals. In another way, it is quite different, because it is a human body. But it is not yet fully a human body. That will happen only when man has arrived at the complete freedom of the glory of the children of God.

In his progress towards himself, man encounters suffering. Suffering is not something which is lived out in the privacy of the individual person. Man always realizes himself in intercourse with his fellows and with the things of the world, in the perspective of that orientation to God which is given to him with his nature. God is in the persons and in the things which encounter me, just as he is in me, also, when I turn towards my fellows and towards things. But it is possible that I may not be living out my vocation, just as it is possible that my fellow will not encounter me in the name of God. In these chaotic personal relationships, things also will be deprived of their meaning. This is the futility to which, according to Rom. viii.20, the creation is subjected, and a theme which Paul connects with "the sufferings of these times."

The eighth chapter of the Letter to the Romans lends itself very well to an appreciation of the suffering of these times in the light of revelation. It is in this chapter that the passage occurs in which Paul goes back to Gen. ii-iii in order to show that creation is subjected to the slavery of decay, the meaning of which we discussed in Chapter 7. The futility to which creation is subject against her will originates in the man who is false to his built-in orientation to God and who worships creatures. As soon as man ignores God and seeks his fulfillment on earth, he loses his dominion over creation. He forgets his eternal destiny, and renders himself transitory. It is not that he ceases to exist, but that he ceases to live, cutting off the way to eternal life, so that he falls back into a meaningless existence that never rises above itself. The capacity created with him is not developed but deformed. Creation, which should lead him to God, turns against him. In this way creation itself ceases to make sense. It is here that suffering enters, and in a form which can be called in-human in the strictest sense of the word. It is a human being who suffers, yet the manner in which he undergoes suffering is inhuman. The suffering is futile and can lead only to despair.

In Rom. viii, Paul is reviewing the situation of man and of creation from the point of view of the salvation which has come through Christ. His description of man and of the world is such as to form the background upon which salvation becomes visible as a new beginning. The Apostle is not dealing with the grace which was effective in the world even before Christ. His viewpoint goes back to principles, not to history. Paul sees man as powerless in himself to escape the dominion of sin and death, and as being, therefore, in no fit state to free creation from meaninglessness. The situation that creation has got into by the complicity of man, who has refused obedience to his Creator, thus becomes an absolutely universal datum, in which the salvation of Christ opens a prospect of being freed.

In this connection the antithesis of spirit and flesh, which is strongly emphasised in Rom. vii-viii, becomes important. The flesh is human existence as negatively qualified. This finds expression particularly in vii.14-25: "We know that the law is spiritual; but I am carnal, sold under sin." (vii.14.) This is the human condition which precedes salvation. Yet this is not the whole condition of man, because in him is heard a powerless but nevertheless audible voice which agrees with the Law. (vii.16.) But the Law, also, remains powerless because the flesh suppresses its voice. (vii.3.) Christ has raised this powerless voice to a mighty sound. His Spirit calls out in us, "Abba, Father!" (viii.15.) Thus the orientation to God is restored in the midst of man's fleshly existence, and the possibility of fulfilling God's will is created. This possibility is no more than a beginning and is deflected by that carnal existence which is marked by sin and death and has impressed upon creation the brand of its decay. Thus in the totality of the actual cosmos and of the society of men there stands the Christian, who on his earthly side is wholly interwoven with the present creation, but who inwardly bears the light which must restore meaning to creation. Paul puts the suffering of these times into this context: "It is the Spirit himself bearing witness with our spirit that we are the children of God, and if children, then heirs, heirs of God, and fellow-heirs with Christ, provided we suffer with him in order that we may be glorified with him. I consider that the sufferings of this present time are not worth comparing with the glory that is to be revealed to us. For the creation waits with eager longing for the revealing of the sons of God; for the creation was subjected to futility, not of its own will but by the will of him who subjected it in hope; because the creation itself will be set free from its bondage to decay and obtain the glorious liberty of the children of God. We know that the whole creation has been groaning in travail together until now; and not only the creation, but we ourselves, who have the first fruits of the Spirit, groan inwardly as we wait for adoption as sons, the redemption of our bodies. For in this hope we were saved. Now hope that is seen is not hope. For who hopes for what he sees? But if we hope for what we do not see, we wait for it with patience." (viii.16-25.)

From the context in which Christian suffering is treated it is clear that this suffering does not consist in incidental contingencies, but that it is given with the state of being a Christian. It consists in the contrast present in man between the spirit—that is, the human spirit restored by the Holy Spirit to its orientation to God—and the flesh, which is the other dimension of man's earthly existence, and equally extends to the depths of the heart. Thus suffering consists in self-denial, to use Jesus' term. Previously man denied himself when he said No to God; he went against his true nature and destiny. Now he has, in the power of the Spirit, to say No to himself, in order to return to the right way. This self-denial, the taking-up of the cross from day to day, is called by Paul the putting to death of the deeds of the body by the power of the Spirit. (Rom. viii.13.) Thus the Christian, in obedience to the Spirit in him, must recover the dominion over the flesh, and, through the flesh, over creation. He must be occupied with this until and in the moment of his death. The Christian must give a meaning to death itself.

For the unbeliever there is absolutely no way of seeing the meaning of death. The fact that an animal dies can be explained biologically. It is also biologically explicable, or at any rate not surprising, that a man should die. That a *man,* as man, should die is, for an unbeliever, quite absurd. This absurdity which atheistic philosophy ascribes to death is a speaking witness to the dignity of man. Only if there were to be a philosophy which could make sense of death without belief in God would atheism have a future.

When a Christian dies, he has to confirm the dominion of

the spirit over the flesh by faith in an enduring bond with God. This faith also says to him that death makes sense, and indeed is a boon. He is always aware that while he is directed to God when still in the earthly body, he cannot know God as he longs to do in the depth of his heart: "We know that while we are at home in the body, we are away from the Lord, for we walk by faith, not by sight." (2 Cor. v.6-7.)

If a man wishes to be saved in the full sense of the word, then it is necessary that a radical change should take place in his existence as a creature. Earthly corporeality must give way to heavenly corporeality: "Just as we have borne the image of the man of dust, we shall also bear the image of the man of heaven." (1 Cor. xv.49.) That is why we wait for the salvation of our bodies. Only when earthly bodily existence has given way to the glorification of the children of God will man be in a condition to consort with God as he has always longed to do. In this life his hope is directed to things unseen, which will be revealed to him after his life.

The new life of the future is thus truly a new creation of God. But it is not discontinuous with the earthly existence of the Christian. The connecting link is the indwelling of the Spirit, which already on earth directs the heart of the Christian to the Father and inscribes on it a new law, the law of love: "For the law of the Spirit of life in Christ Jesus has set me free from the law of sin and death. . . . If the Spirit of him who raised Christ Jesus from the dead dwells in you, he who raised Christ Jesus from the dead will give life to your mortal bodies also through his Spirit which dwells in you." (Rom. viii.2, 11.)

In this way dying becomes an act full of meaning even for the Christian who meets with a sudden death and has no time to realize what is happening to him. Death becomes meaningful through the Christian life itself, as the Christian lives it in his daily actions. The Christian who denies himself, and kills the habits of the flesh by the power of the Spirit of God, is a man already busied with putting off the body of dust, uprooting the old man and putting on the new. In doing this he has already defined his position in respect of death. No additional act is required to transform death into a meaningful event.

The sufferings of this time have many facets which in the end can all be reduced to the earthly experience of man's relation to God. Given that God is the Invisible, and that man is clothed in dust, the orientation to God, which the Spirit has awakened in the human heart, will be able to express itself in earthly life only in our contacts with our visible fellow men. "But if anyone has the world's goods and sees his brother in need, yet closes his heart against him, how does God's love abide in him? Little children, let us not love in word or speech but in deed and truth. No one has ever seen God; if we love one another, God abides in us and his love is perfected in us. By this we know that we abide in him and he in us, because he has given us his own Spirit." (1 John iii.17-18; iv.12-13.)

In the mutual love of Christians an element of suffering

is present, to the extent that in this love the Christian gives himself, his person, and his possessions. One or the other struggles with the old man in us. We are truly busy dying to ourselves, as regards the aspiration of the "flesh." But suffering comes to us also from the other side. It comes to us especially from our fellows, just as we also can be a burden to others. The classical example in Holy Scripture is persecution for the Faith. The Christian is tried by persecution. If he yields to violence, then his trials reveal that his love of God was deficient. But to endure trials, and especially to suffer death in order to confess Christ, is the highest self-affirmation of the spirit in our earthly life, and at the same time the freest act which man can attain to on earth.

Trials can also present themselves in the form of sickness, and all sorts of setbacks which do not come from ourselves or our fellows. Here, too, a martyrdom is consummated in which the Christian must bear witness to his faith in eternal life. Earthly existence is essentially a trial which requires a constant affirmation of belief in God, which offers us an opportunity, precisely through the trial, to win freedom for ourselves. In this way, man learns to rule over creation, which now can no longer harm him. Creation shows that it is good: "We know that in everything God works for good with those who love him." (Rom. viii.28.) The Christian who is truly held by Christ knows that nothing can threaten him any more. "Who shall separate us from the love of Christ? Shall tribulation, or distress, or persecution, or famine, or nakedness, or peril, or the sword? As it is written, 'For thy sake we are being killed all day long; we are regarded as sheep to be slaughtered.' No, in all these things we are more than conquerors through him who loved us. For I am sure that neither death, nor life, nor angels, nor principalities, nor things present, nor things to come, nor powers, nor height, nor depth, nor anything else in all creation, will be able to separate us from the love of God in Christ Jesus our Lord." (Rom. viii.35-9.)

Man can withstand trials because in this Jesus has gone before him. We have already spoken about this in connection with the Letter to the Hebrews. Still, I should like to come back to one aspect of Christ's work of salvation which sheds a very clear light on how Christ's life of self-dedication to God and his fellow men results in a new creation, consisting in the victory over fleshly existence by a union with God unveiled.

In Rom. viii.25 Paul says that our expectation of salvation goes together with constancy, because our hope is in the invisible. The author of Hebrews also entertains this thought: "We have this as a sure and steadfast anchor of the soul, a hope that enters into the inner shrine behind the curtain, where Jesus has gone as a forerunner on our behalf, having become a high priest for ever after the order of Melchizedek." (Heb. vi.19-20.)

The curtain plays an important part in the Letter to the Hebrews. In the economy of salvation of the Old Covenant, God's presence was inaccessible, something which was symbolized by the institution of the sanctuary. God lived in the Holy of the Holies, but his indwelling was cut off from the people by a curtain. The sacrificial way of Christ is described on the analogy of the liturgy which the Levitical high priest performed on the great day of atonement. But Christ has gone through the curtain and abides eternally with God. He is "behind the curtain" (vi.19), unlike the high priest, who annually entered only to return again.

In x.19-20 the author concludes his doctrinal expositions concerning the sacrifice of Christ by indicating to Christians the way to God, which now lies open to them: "Therefore, brethren, since we have confidence to enter the sanctuary by the blood of Jesus, by the new and living way which he opened for us through the curtain, that is, through his flesh . . . let us draw near with a true heart." Here it is affirmed that Jesus made a way through the curtain of his mortal body, literally, "of his flesh." Fleshly existence is here indicated to be the curtain which was hung between the earthly Jesus and God. It is at the same time a human existence in "flesh and blood" through which Jesus belongs to our generation. Now the curtain is no longer a barrier. It is not done away with, because Jesus remains always man, even in his glorification. But the curtain has become penetrable by virtue of the divine life that was in Jesus, and by the eternal Spirit by which he gave himself as a spotless offering to God. (ix.14.) Humanity on earth still stands before the curtain, and does not yet see what is behind it. But the anchor of its hope is already cast out, because Christ is there. The curtain is the fashion of this world which passes away, to which our corporeality belongs and to which the corporeality of Jesus also once belonged.

If, after this consideration of the meaning of suffering, we still emphatically raise the theme of evolution, it will be to confirm that suffering is an important factor in evolution immediately the latter reaches the human level. Suffering is the modality of the human stage on the way to its perfection, and provides man with the possibility, in obedience to the inspiration of God, of achieving the freedom in which, as perfected man, he shall possess himself for ever in freedom. Trials put humanity in a position to gain dominion over its fleshly existence, and in this way also to gain dominion over creation.

When man, in this disposition, knows how to turn death into a personal act, he will, in another life, be the perfected heavenly man for whom creation has become transparent as the revelation of God. On earth, things are already inspirited by the love which expresses itself through them. In the future it will come to pass that people will communicate with each other, and all together with Christ, in a world which we can see in complete clarity.

# 11

# THE VISION OF GOD

In the constitution *Benedictus Deus* of 29 January 1336, Pope Benedict XII confirmed as the teaching of the Church that the justified dead "shortly after death," or after purgatorial purification, should they need it, "after the suffering and death of the Lord Jesus Christ, saw and see the divine Being in a direct vision and face to face, without the mediation of any creature, since the divine Being reveals himself immediately to them, unveiled, clearly and openly." In Catholic teaching about the last things this pronouncement is a very important datum. Its central point lies in this, that the sleep of the soul after death is denied, and that the vision of God is attributed to "the souls of all who are sanctified." This seeing of God is immediate. Then God will no more be known through the medium of any created reality.

Shortly before that, John XXII, in the constitution *In Agro Dominico* of 27 March 1329, had condemned the error of Eckhart, according to whom "we are totally transformed into God, and changed into him, in the same manner as in the Sacrament the bread is changed into the body of Christ. I am so changed into him, that he transforms me into his very being, and not into a similar being. In the living God, it is true, there will be no single difference [between God and man]."

In speaking of the vision of God we are skirting the abyss of pantheism. In the course of history the mystics again and again display the tendency to word their experience in statements with a pantheistic ring. Eckhart is an example of this. To circumvent this danger we must put it very clearly that the definition of Benedict XII does not try to affirm that the sanctified will know God through and through, that is, "comprehensively," as theology expresses it. If that were so, the transcendence of God would be denied. Such a knowledge is proper only to the Son, who lives with the Father in the communion of the Holy Spirit. But here we are outside the created order.

That the vision of the sanctified does not reach to the being of God in his divine Infinity, while yet being a vision in unmediated presence, rests upon this, that the sanctified are creatures. The revelation which comes to them from the side of God is a creative revelation. It never reaches to a pantheistic fusion with God, because (since in all his works God is the Creator) his unveiled self-revelation necessarily places the creature at an absolute distance from his Infinity.

Man will therefore never know God in any other way than as Creator. He will see the Trinity, by whom he is made. The creature will, in a creaturely mode, know his Creator. That is the boundary line laid down for us, over which we shall never pass. It is absurd to posit that God from his side will cross the boundary by a total and exhaustive self-revelation. Thus we have arrived again at the coming forth of the eternal Word from the Father.

Hence though the object of knowledge in the Beatific Vision is God in unveiled self-communication, the knowledge itself is a created reality, because it is human knowledge. If we wish to avoid pantheism, we shall have to affirm these two truths simultaneously: the sanctified see God in immediate vision, but their knowledge is circumscribed by the limits of the creature. The immediacy and the limitedness both belong to our vision of God.

But if the knowledge which the sanctified have of God is limited, then the immediate self-revelation of God must also be limited. Now what is a limited self-revelation of God? It is certain that God gives himself to be known unveiled, but how can this occur in a limited way?

Revelation provides us with an answer when it points to the incarnate Son of God, who is the only Mediator between God and man. The Son of God has come down to earth to reveal the Father. "No one has ever seen God; the only Son, who is in the bosom of the Father, he has made him known." (John i.18.) And Jesus himself says: "He who has seen me has seen the Father." (John xiv.9.) What is spoken of here is knowledge by faith, which the Apostles have of Jesus, and not the Beatific Vision. Nevertheless we must pause upon the words of Jesus, because they are perhaps not grapsed in their full depth.

We are accustomed to the idea that the Son of God, through the Incarnation, became visible on earth. This follows from the mystery of the Hypostatic Union, on the basis of which we see this man as the Son of God. The Son of God has assumed human nature, so that he who sees the man, Jesus, sees the Son of God. But when wc havc said this we have not said everything, because "seeing" can be understood in two ways.

We can understand it in this way, that we see the human nature, of which we confess that it belongs to the Son of God in hypostatic union. Then we do not *see* any more than the human nature which we hold in faith to be united with the Son of God, who is the subject of it. But then we can no longer understand how Jesus can say, "He who has seen me has seen the Father." We do see the Son, because human nature belongs to him. But we do not see the Father, since the Father is not subject of the Incarnation. The words of Jesus only receive their full meaning if we accept that he who perceives the human nature *simultaneously* also sees the Son, who becomes visible in the human nature. We then see the Son of God himself in the veiled revelation of his earthly body. Just as the human spirit in our fellow men appears to us in a bodily way, so the Son of God appears in a human way to those whom he teaches. The intuition of the unity of man helps to clarify our ideas about our intuition of the unity of Christ. Only then does it become clear that he who sees the Son also sees the Father, because the Son, who in his incarnation appears on earth, is the Image of the Father. The invisible God becomes visible on earth through the incarnation of the Son. This interpretation of the Fourth Gospel is usual among the Fathers, especially the Greek Fathers of the Alexandrian school. It places the accent differently from scholastic Christology, though it would take us too far out of our way to pursue this.

The difference is, however, very important for our exposition, because what is completed on earth in Jesus will occur, in an analogous fashion, in the Beatific Vision. The mediatorship of Jesus will then not cease but will attain its eternal form. Then the glorified Lord will be he who reveals the Father to us. If we propose that in the Beatific Vision we shall see the Son of God without his humanity, we damage the mediatorship of Christ at the core. "And this is eternal life, that they know thee, the only true God, and *Jesus Christ* whom thou hast sent. I glorified thee on earth, having accomplished the work which thou gavest me to do; and now, Father, glorify thou me in thy own presence with the glory which I had with thee before the world was made." (John xvii.3-5.) The vision of the Son of God remains, in the life of eternity, the vision of Jesus Christ. His becoming man is not unmade again. But then, and in the human nature of Jesus, the glory will be revealed which is proper to him as the Son of God. There is thus a real vision of the Son of God *according to his divine glory,* but this glory is seen in the Son made man.

Other texts in the New Testament point in the same direction, and the clearest is 1 Tim. vi.13-16: "In the presence of God who gives life to all things, and of Christ Jesus who in his testimony before Pontius Pilate made the good confession, I charge you to keep the commandment unstained and free from reproach *until the appearing of our Lord Jesus Christ; and this will be made manifest at the proper time by the blessed and only Sovereign,* the King of Kings, and Lord of lords, who alone has immortality and dwells in unapproachable light, *whom no man has ever seen or can see.* To him be honor and eternal dominion. Amen."

In the last verse Paul is not speaking about the earthly man. He is talking about the *epiphaneia,* the second coming of Christ, seen as a manifestation. Outside of this manifestation God remains the hidden and unapproachable. But he shows Jesus Christ, "the Image of the invisible God." (Col. i.15.)

Does this not contradict what Benedict XII laid down when he said that the saints see God face to face, while no creature mediates here as the object of the vision? No, because what is there repudiated is that the saints in their vision do not meet God himself, but only the creature. We should then not be able to say that they see God immediately. The view of the Beatific Vision just set out seems to me fully to satisfy the two conditions which are required of this vision by orthodox faith: immediacy and limitation.

Should we say that the vision of the Son of God in his humanity lacks the character of an immediate vision, we should show that we did not understand what is meant by saying that Christ is *one*. Just as little, then, should we comprehend that the man who sees Christ is *one*. We should have to interpret the resurrection of the sanctified as a hindrance to the vision of God. We should then fall into the way of Calvin, who puts forward the opinion (*Institutions,* ii, 14, 3) that the Son of God after the Judgment will put off his human nature, to let his divine glory freely radiate before the eyes of the saints. What we should have left is a Beatific Vision in which neither the humanity of Christ nor the whole of the human nature of the saints played a part. In either case we do not really know what to do with the corporeality of Christ and the sanctified. Theology shows this only too clearly: the resurrection, of which St. Paul speaks on every page, is reduced to an inessential occurrence.

The divine glory, which the Son possesses from eternity and in which he is one with the Father, is seen immediately in the glorified Lord, but not in the unlimited way in which the Son knows the Father and the Father the Son. It is seen in a fashion limited by the Incarnation, which is accessible to the creature. The sanctified do not see anything created that stands between them and the divine glory, but they see *together* the divine glory and the created human nature of Christ. They see both immediately, and their knowledge of God is at once immediate and limited.

The glorified Christ is the mediator of the happiness of the saints. In him they have a way to the vision of the

Father. Being with the Lord is for St. Paul the same as the life of vision. "So we are always of good courage; we know that while we are at home in the body we are away from the Lord, for we walk by faith, not by sight. We are of good courage, and we would rather be away from the body and at home with the Lord." (2 Cor. v.6-8.) The body, here, is the earthly body, "the earthly tent we live in" (v.1). In Phil. i.21-3 he calls the earthly manner of existence "flesh." "For to me to live is Christ, and to die is gain. If it is to be life in the flesh, that means fruitful labour for me. Yet which I shall choose I cannot tell. I am hard pressed between the two. My desire is to depart and be with Christ, for that is far better." But here, too, being with Christ is a comprehension of future happiness.

By this conception of the Beatific Vision we have not only solved the meaning of the Incarnation for salvation, but, at the same time, that of the visible creation, to which the humanity of Christ forever belongs, a meaning bestowed before the self-revelation of God to the sanctified. In Chapter 1 we spoke about the two ways of knowing God, and considered particularly the knowledge of earthly men, that is, of the believer who sees the veiled presence of the Creator in the visible creation. In the two phases of the evolution of man, his knowledge of God is changed to an unveiled seeing of the Creator in his creation. Here also it holds that the saints know God in the creature in the sense that they *simultaneously* see God and the creature. The creature itself is the immediate and unveiled presence of

God in relation to the saints. It is necessarily the creaturely measure according to which the saints know God, because by virtue of their existence as creatures they are tied to this limit. No other knowledge of God is possible for man than a knowledge in creation. The highest to which man can reach is to see creation as the unveiled presence of God.

When the godly of the Old Covenant hymned the divine Wisdom, they said that God alone saw Wisdom, and fathomed and counted it, when he looked out to the bounds of the earth and saw everything which existed under heaven. In Job xxviii the technical achievements and the knowledge of nature of those times are depicted as quite inadequate to trace the play of Wisdom in creation, and the way it follows among creatures.

Surely there is a mine for silver,
and a place for gold which they refine.
Iron is taken out of the earth,
and copper is smelted from the ore.
Men put an end to darkness,
and search out to the farthest bound
the ore in gloom and deep darkness.
They open shafts in a valley away from where men live;
they are forgotten by travellers,
they hang afar from men, they swing to and fro.
As for the earth, out of it comes bread;
but underneath it is turned up as by fire.
Its stones are the place of sapphires,
and it has dust of gold.
That path no bird of prey knows,

and the falcon's eye has not seen it.
The proud beasts have not trodden it;
the lion has not passed over it.
Man puts his hand to the flinty rock,
and overturns mountains by the roots.
He cuts out channels in the rocks,
and his eye sees every precious thing.
He binds up the streams so that they do not trickle,
and the things that are hid he brings forth to light.
But where shall wisdom be found?
And where is the place of understanding?
Man does not know the way to it,
and it is not found in the land of the living.
The deep says, "It is not in me,"
and the sea says, "It is not with me."
It is hid from the eyes of all living,
and concealed from the birds of the air.
Abaddon and Death say,
"We have heard a rumour of it with our ears."
God understands the way to it,
and he knows its place.
For he looks to the ends of the earth,
and sees everything under the heavens.
When he gave to the wind its weight
and meted out the waters by measure;
when he made a decree for the rain,
and a way for the lightning of the thunder;
then he saw it and declared it;
he established it and searched it out.

[Job xxviii.1-14, 21-7]

What is mentioned in this lovely song as strictly reserved for God, man will be able to see in the future life. He will be able to see the Wisdom of God, and fathom and count it in the creation which exists by her. It is not as it was earlier, when she made the circuit of the vault of heaven alone and walked in the depth of the ocean. (Ecclus. xxiv.5.) Now all the children of Wisdom will be able to accompany her. The creation which she left with death, she re-enters in an unimaginably new way. The universe becomes the dwelling of the children of Wisdom forever, no longer the universe which speaks of God in veiled words, so that man can serve it as an idol, but the universe as they see it being created by God. God radiates upon them unveiled from men and things. And the glory of God lies in the face of Jesus Christ (2 Cor. iv.6), who has also ascended far above all the heavens, that he may fill all things. (Eph. iv.10.)

All this happens because, in the sanctified, Jesus has become the light of the world in a new way. The world is not changed, but they are changed. The same world which is trodden by mortals is paradise for the saints. The faithful in the Catholic Church speak to the saints as if they were present. And that is correct, because our world is also their world, but they possess this world in its totality, the world with the plants and animals, with the mountain-tops and the ocean depths, with the sun and moon and stars, to the very depths of the universe. All creatures, by virtue of the salvation made apparent in Christ, have received a share of the glory of the children of God, and are freed from the slavery of transience. What the poets said about creation as the revelation of God to the godly becomes actuality, in a new and higher way.

> Thy steadfast love, O Lord, extends to the heavens,
> thy faithfulness to the clouds.
> Thy righteousness is like the mountains of God,
> thy judgments are like the great deep;
> man and beast thou savest, O Lord.
> How precious is thy steadfast love, O God!
> The children of men take refuge in the shadow of thy wings.
> They feast on the abundance of thy house,
> and thou givest them drink from the river of thy delights.
> For with thee is the fountain of life;
> in thy light do we see light.
>
> [Ps. xxxvi.5-9]

"In thy light do we see light." At the end of time it will come about that the interior light, springing up in the sanctified from the divine Wisdom, will shine out over all earthly light:

> The sun shall be no more
> your light by day,
> nor for brightness shall the moon
> give light to you by night;
> but the Lord will be your everlasting light,
> and your days of mourning shall be ended.
>
> [Isa. lx.19-20]

In the present world there is a natural longing for the sight of God. It is the light of reason turned to God, and seeing creatures as God's creation. Corresponding to this is the manner in which creation presents itself to man, with the light that is in him. Just as the light which is in man is confined by the body of earth in which it appears, so man sees things in a way which corresponds to his present way of existence as earthly. But even so, things present themselves as knowable because they have been raised out of nothingness and given order by the Wisdom which is the light of man, so that they can be known as God's creation. The light of human reason, which equates with the desire for the vision of God, glimpses the presence of God in things, but it is a presence veiled in earthly forms, just as human reason itself is limited by our terrestrial manner of existence.

Obviously that holds of the whole of creation which man perceives. The sun speaks to him of God, but through the physical light that it radiates, and which functions physically, man goes about unfolding and perfecting his earthly existence. This is the *natural revelation* of God which is creative in the way in which it supports man's terrestrial life. That is why man must praise and thank God for the creatures which make his life on earth possible. The early Christians enjoyed their meals together in joyfulness and simplicity of heart, praising God and having favour with the people. (Acts ii.46-7.) That is why St. Paul can say of the present existence of men: "In him we live and move and have our being; as even some of your poets have said, For we are indeed his offspring." (Acts xvii.28.) The world in which and out of which we live is the veiled presence of God. This we know because his light is in us.

Those who will not acknowledge the truth also experience the creative goodness of God by means of the world. God makes his sun to rise over the evil and the good, and his rain to fall upon the righteous and the unrighteous. In this way he teaches us, who believe in him, to do good to our enemies (Matt. v.43-8), and by his patience he converts the unbelievers.

> But thou art merciful to all, for thou canst do all things
> and thou dost overlook men's sins, that they may repent.
> For thou lovest all things that exist,
> and hast loathing for none of the things which thou hast made,
> for thou wouldst not have made anything if thou hadst hated it.
> How would anything have endured if thou hadst not willed it?
> Or how would anything not called forth by thee have been preserved?
> Thou sparest all things, for they are thine, O Lord who lovest the living.
>
> [Wisd. of Sol. xi.23-6]

But when this time has passed away, then those who deny God will confront a very different experience of the universe:

The Lord will take his zeal as his whole armour,
and will arm all creation to repel his enemies;
he will put on righteousness as a breastplate,
and wear impartial justice as a helmet;
he will take holiness as an invincible shield,
and sharpen stern wrath for a sword,
and creation will join with him to fight against the madmen.
[Wisd. of Sol. v.17-20]

That very creation which is experienced by the saints as paradise will be a torture to sinners.

In the future world Christ will be the light of man in an entirely new way. The new light first shone out in Christ himself as a creaturely participation of the eternal Light of which, in his divinity, he is the radiation. Christ's humanity continues wholly to belong to the creation, and the light that is in him is also a creaturely participation of the eternal Light. The dogma of the Hypostatic Union requires that we distinguish the human and divine natures. That is why, in the human nature of Christ, there is nothing divine in the exact sense. The light of human reason in Christ is also a created light, and when the sanctified share in this light, then that is also created light. Thus an exhaustive knowledge of God cannot be arrived at. It cannot reach the inaccessible Light. But it is able to reach that on which the longing of our earthly intelligence is fixed: the knowledge of God as the Creator of his creatures. Just as the light of the man to be is limited by his creatureliness, so he can perceive God only within the limits of the creature. Thus we come back to the truth which we formulated above when we said that no other knowledge of God is possible than a knowledge of God in creation.

Herein is founded the fact that evolution proceeds after our deaths as well, for it is endless, just because men cannot reach him who inhabits the inaccessible Light. And man does not wish to reach it, because to see it does not accord with his nature as creature. That is why it is sufficient for the believer "to depart and be with Christ." (Phil. i.23.)

In this companionship with Christ, the saints walk the universe to view the wonders of God. They are no longer pilgrims and strangers, but have reached their fatherland. They walk in God's garden in his unveiled company, and every encounter with men and things is a new revelation and therefore a new creation. God's creative work goes on.

The representation of the Beatific Vision which I have given above is very imperfect. It becomes apparent mainly from this, that I have described it upon the analogy of an ordinary play, where the spectator stands over against what he sees. I presented it as if the saint were confronting Christ, and as if Christ were looking at the Father as if he were "over there." That this representation must be called inadequate follows from a closer analysis of the Beatific Vision. We, with our earthly thoughts, must speak here only with great hesitation, having in mind the words of the Apostle: "No eye has seen, nor ear heard, nor the heart of man conceived, what God has prepared for those who love him." (1 Cor. ii.9.) Thus we are speaking here in a purely speculative manner, and with the purpose of preserving the infinite distance between Creator and creature. What the vision of God means as an experience is totally hidden from us.

God is known in creation. We can, as we have repeatedly done above, think of the creation, in which God appears, as an object of knowledge. In this sense we can say that the humanity of Christ is the object of the saint's knowledge; and the same holds of the whole of creation. But we can also regard the creation, in which God appears, from the side of the knowing subject, perpetually being created. Christ and the sanctified, by virtue of their human and created intelligence, are the subject of the vision of God. This is also a sense in which God is known in creation, namely, in the human understanding of the knowing subject.

This latter conception approaches much closer to reality than the first. The saint, who sees God in Christ, does not see God over against him, but within himself. The Known is in the knower. God is in the created subject who knows him. Herein lies the only foundation of the truth that God is known only within the limitation of the creature. A created intelligence cannot comprehend the fullness of God. That is why God is known only according to the capacity of the knowing subject.

We must interpret this capacity concretely, and as the capacity of the *human* understanding, or better, of the human spirit, or, in the language of the Bible, of the human *heart.* We must not forget the will. In the Bible both willing and knowing originate in the heart, and those two are one, just as their point of origin is one. Biblical "knowing" is laden with affectivity.

God communicates himself to the human heart in the subjective experience of knowledge and love. The happiness which we feel on earth at seeing something lovely, or in the love we have of somebody, consists entirely in subjective experience. That is quite clear. So it must also be when we see God. Here also happiness consists in subjective experience, and it is precisely in this experience that God reveals himself. The human experience of knowing and loving is the creaturely measure of the vision of God unveiled.

Even Christ cannot comprehend the infinity of God from the side of his human spirit. The limitation is set by the fact that the human spirit of Christ is a creature. Christ knows and loves God in the measure that God as the Known and the Loved can communicate himself to his human understanding. In the life of the Trinity the Son has an actual infinite knowledge and love of the Father, and the Father gives the Son the fullness of his Life. The divine relation of the Father and the Son now shines through the prism of human nature, in which it becomes the subjective experience of the man Christ. The immediate vision of God by Christ is *the incarnation* of God in him.

These remarks not only render precise the conception "vision of God" but are at the same time a good introduction to the exegesis of certain texts from the New Testament which are quoted in all treatments of this subject. The best-known is presumably 1 John iii.2: ". . . but we know that when he appears we shall be like him, for we shall see him as he is."

The First Letter of John says a great deal about the mutual love of Christians, and in my opinion this should be our point of departure for understanding the text about the vision of God, and all the more because the preceding passage (iii.1) expressly speaks about love.

In reading the New Testament one is struck by the fact that love towards God is hardly mentioned. And if ever it is mentioned, it is immediately accompanied by the statement that there is another command *like to* the first (Matt. xxii.37-40); or at any rate it is pointed out to us that we must not think that we love God if we hate our neighbour. "If anyone says, 'I love God,' and hates his brother, he is a liar; for he who does not love his brother, whom he has seen, cannot love God whom he has not seen. And this commandment we have from him, that he who loves God should love his brother also." (1 John iv.20-21.) Here again we find the thought that nobody has seen God. The only possible way of meeting him is through his creatures—in this instance, our neighbours.

Although we do not see God, as is said elsewhere in the letter, yet we on earth can really know him. We know him in the love which is in us. "Beloved, let us love one another; for love is of God, and he who loves is born of God and knows God. He who does not love does not know God; for

God is love." (1 John iv.7-8.) There is on earth, then, no knowledge or love of God except by means of the creation in which we meet God. It is an experiential knowledge of God. In the love which we bear our neighbour, we experience the presence of God. God reveals himself to us in love, and this love is creative. Because love evokes an answer or is itself an answer, Christians who love one another on earth are the creators of each other, because they reveal God to each other. Especially is the love of our enemies a creative love.

The spring of this love lies in God, the Invisible. He has made his love visible in Christ. "In this the love of God was made manifest among us, that God sent his only Son into the world, so that we might live through him. In this is love, not that we loved God but that he loved us and sent his Son to be the expiation of our sins." (iv.9-10.) The love of Christ for man is the revelation of the love of God for man. It is the "love of God in Jesus Christ our Lord." (Rom. viii.39.) Therefore, if we will to encounter the love of God, then we shall only be able to reach this love in its revelation in Christ, in "the love of Christ which surpasses all knowledge." (Eph. iii.19.)

It is against this background that we must read and comprehend 1 John iii.1: "See what love the Father has given us, that we should be called the children of God; and so we are." He who loves is born of God, is a child of God. All this is a gift of the Father. He has given us his Son as the revelation of his love. (John iii.16). He who follows the

Son lives from him. Such a one "has passed out of death into life because he loves the brethren." (1 John iii.14.) The love which the Father reveals in his Son becomes the portion of Christians. There is a movement which goes out from the Father and goes through Christ to take shape in the mutual love of Christians. Thus we must understand the words: "See what love the Father has given us" (iii.1) as referring to the love of neighbour which God gives to Christians through the mediation of Christ. Then there follows: "Beloved, we are God's children now; it does not yet appear what we shall be, but we know that when he appears we shall be like him, for we shall see him as he is." (iii.2.)

Without doubt what is being referred to is the coming revelation of Christ. The verb "reveal himself" is used in ii.28 of the *parousia* of Christ. The verses which follow iii.2 clearly refer to Christ. Nowhere in the letter is there mention of an immediate revelation of God. The Apostle is thus stating that there is already on earth a certain likeness of the incarnate Son of God in the love which Christians have for one another. By virtue of it they are, with the Son, already really children of God. But in the future, when Christ reveals himself, Christians will themselves be like him because they will see him as he is. Seeing that the reference is to Christ, we can take these words at their full meaning without falling into pantheism. The saints see Christ as he is. Christ is the image of God. He who sees Christ, therefore, sees the Father, but in the figure of Christ.

In this life Christians know God in the love which they

bear one another, and which they have received through Christ. They have a share in the love which is in Christ. This knowledge of God is not a looking at something over against them, but the subjective experience of encountering their neighbour. The one Christian loves the other through the love of Christ which is in them both. Christ truly lives in both, but he has not yet become revealed. When Christ reveals himself that will mean that Christians will meet each other unveiled in Christ.

John sees the earthly knowledge which the believer has of Christ actualized in the experience of the Christian who loves his neighbour. In the after-life this knowledge passes into vision. The sanctified see Christ as he is. This they can do because there is a light in them which makes this vision possible. They themselves will have changed. How that will be we have at present no idea, because "what we shall be is not yet revealed to us." The revelation of what the Christian will be coincides with the coming of Christ in revelation. "When Christ who is our life appears, then you also will appear with him in glory." (Col. iii.4.)

We see that John, in 1 John iii.1-2, first speaks about the love that the Father has given to the faithful, and then mentions the vision which will make the believer like Christ in the future life. There is no more mention of love. Yet there must be a connection between the gift of love, which the Christian already receives on earth, and the vision of Christ in the future life. We know from this letter that John regards the love of Christians as a revelation of God: he who loves knows God, for God is love. Conversely we can also say that the vision of God in Christ will likewise consist in the experience of love. Just as the experience of love on earth is already a *knowledge* of God, so the *seeing* of God in Christ consists in an experience of love, but of a love which goes together with an unveiled seeing.

Love is the presence of the Spirit of God. (iii.24; iv.13.) In the whole of this chapter we have not yet said anything about the Holy Spirit, because the texts which we have been discussing did not lead into that subject. But this does not mean that the Holy Spirit does not play his part in the vision of God. It has already been pointed out in Chapter 8 that, according to the Old Testament, the orientation of man to God comes from the Spirit of God, and that seen from God's side, the Spirit is the creative gaze with which God sees his creature. Hence the parallelism between the Spirit and the Face of God. The mutual relation between God and man is through the Spirit.

This is all relevant where the vision of God is concerned. We have constantly spoken about God who reveals himself to man, and about man who sees God. The union which thus arises between God and man is through the Spirit.

We must thus conclude that the vision of God in the other life will consist in the union of the sanctified with Christ unveiled. In this vision they will take part in what Christ is. Indeed, they will be like him. Through the Spirit they will experience the love of Christ for the Father, and the Father for Christ. The last sentence of Jesus' high-priestly prayer runs: "I have made known to them thy name, and I will make it known, that the love with which thou hast loved me may be in them, and I in them." (John xvii.26.) Where we read the word "love" we think of the Holy Spirit. In the co-experience of the love with which Christ loves the Father, and which answers to the love which goes out from the Father to Christ, the mystery of the divine Trinity is revealed to the sanctified. For this love is the presence of the Spirit. The sanctified will possess this experience in common, for he who co-experiences what Christ is will meet in his sanctified fellows those in whom Christ lives, and also the creation which exists through him.

In 1 Cor. xiii we find the same transition from Christian love to the vision face to face. There love is the all-inclusive bond which gives their value to all the other gifts. Knowledge, faith, and generosity—all these only mean something when carried by love. Love alone endures. The other things, namely knowledge and prophecy, shall make way for sight. "For we see in a mirror dimly, but then face to face. Now I know in part; then I shall understand fully, even as I have been fully understood." (*v.* 12). Here again one asks oneself whether, in this seeing face to face, love still plays a part. The confirmatory answer lies to hand, for, indeed, the Apostle has already spoken of the love that never perishes. Elsewhere in this letter he writes: "'Knowledge' puffs up, but love builds up. If anyone imagines that he knows something, he does not yet know as he ought to know. But if one loves God, one is known by him." (1 Cor. viii.1-3.) Paul wants to tell us that on earth there is not yet any real knowledge, certainly not if this knowledge leads to conceit. But what does exist is *loving,* and *being known.* Further, in Gal. iv.9 he withdraws what he says about knowing God in order to substitute for it, being known by God: "But now that you have come to know God, or rather to be known by God . . ." On earth it becomes the Christian to exercise love, for then he is known by God. In the next life, "I shall understand fully, even as I have been fully understood." He who loves is known, but does not himself know in the manner in which God knows him. But then love will pass over into sight, and from being a veiled, will become an unveiled, knowledge of God by experience.

And I saw no temple in the city, for its temple is the Lord God the Almighty and the Lamb: And the city has no need of sun or moon to shine upon it, for the glory of God is its light, and its lamp is the Lamb. By its light shall the nations walk; and the kings of the earth shall bring their glory into it, and its gates shall never be shut by day—and there shall be no night there; they shall bring into it the glory and the honour of the nations. But nothing unclean shall enter it, or anyone who practices abomination or falsehood, but only those who are written in the Lamb's book of life.

Then he showed me the river of the water of life, bright as crystal, flowing from the throne of God and of the Lamb through the middle of the street of the city; also, on either side of the river, the tree of life with its twelve kinds of fruit, yielding its fruit each month; and the leaves of the tree were for the healing of the nations. There shall no more be anything accursed, but the throne of God and of the Lamb shall be in it, and his servants shall worship him; they shall see his face, and his name shall be on their foreheads. And night shall be no more; they need no light of lamp or sun, for the Lord God shall be their light, and they shall reign for ever and ever. [Rev. xxi.22-xxii.5.]

Within the place of the holy city there shall be paradise again. The whole creation will then consist of "trees of life" by which the nations will live.

# 12

# THE CHURCH

In the previous chapter we encountered several passages of Scripture where it was said that Christians on earth are known by God, but do not themselves really know God. God knows the Christian fully, but the Christian knows God in a veiled manner. These texts form part of a broad concordance of passages which reach back into the Old Testament. In these related texts the word *pleroma* or "fullness" occurs, a word which, in the letters to the Christians of Ephesus and Colossae, sometimes occurs together with *ekklesia* or "church." This is enough to indicate by what road I wish to approach the notion of *ekklesia.*

The most remote point of departure for our exposition is the Old Testament conception of God's lordship over the universe. Yahweh is King of Israel, of all nations, and of the universe. According to the Old Testament writers God's lordship consists in his *creative knowledge* of the universe. A clear example of this view occurs in Job 28, a text we have quoted several times. God looks out to the limits of the earth when he determines the laws of the phenomena of nature. Then he sees his multiple wisdom in creation. By means of his wisdom—thus, of his knowledge—he creates and orders the universe:

> The Lord by wisdom founded the earth;
> by understanding he established the heavens;
> by his knowledge the deep broke forth,
> and the clouds drop down the dew.
>
> [Prov. iii.19-20]

By this means one can show that the omniscience of God is bound up with his creative omnipresence. Ps. 139 is a splendid example of this. It commences with the words "O Lord, thou hast searched me and known me." Then, in *v.* 13, the ground of this omniscience is stated: "For thou didst form my inward parts, thou didst knit me together in my mother's womb." Then the psalmist goes on to praise the vast sum of God's thoughts (*vv.* 17-18), something which reminds us of the immeasurability of Wisdom, which can be fathomed only by God. Jer. xxiii.24 is another example: "Can a man hide himself in secret places so that I cannot see him? says the Lord. Do I not fill heaven and earth? says the Lord." We find an echo of this in Wisd. of Sol. i.7-8: "Because the Spirit of the Lord has filled the world, and that which holds all things together knows what is said; therefore no one who utters unrighteous things will escape notice."

God is the sovereign Lord of all that is created, because as Creator he plumbs everything to the roots of its being. He creates through his wisdom, which is his ordaining power of creation. To know creation and to make it exist are one and the same.

This is connected with the fact that God fills heaven and earth. (Jer. xxiii.24.) The word "fills" can lead us into error here; we may think that heaven and earth are there, and that Yahweh then fills them with his presence. The verb here is simply "fills," that is, to make full, as one would fill a jug with water. Yahweh fills the universe. But in the case of the universe, there is nothing precedent to be filled up. Creation itself is the filling. Creation itself, the visible universe, is the presence of Yahweh. God presents himself by creating, and he who sees creation, sees God in a veiled way. The expression "I fill heaven and earth" is repeated elsewhere in other words: "The earth, O Lord, is full of thy steadfast love" (Ps. cxix.64); "The earth is the Lord's and the fullness thereof, the world and those who dwell therein." (Ps. xxiv.1.)

God is Lord of all by knowing it creatively, and creating it knowingly. He expresses himself in his *wisdom,* and by way of his wisdom in *creation*. Creation as the presence of God is thus the wisdom of God become the world. He who looks at creation gets an idea of the multiple wisdom of God, and therefore of God himself. The creation is a forerunner of the Incarnation: "He who sees me, sees the Father." (John xiv.9.) The disciples see a man, and in this man they see the Son of God. In this way they come to see the Father, of whom the Son is the image. It is the same with the creation. He who sees creation sees the wisdom of God in veiled presentation, and he who sees Wisdom sees the wise Creator. We must not understand this pantheistically, any more than we must understand the word of Jesus as the Monophysites did. When we say that the Son of God appears as man, and when it is said of the Apostles that they have touched the Word of Life with their hands (1 John i.1), it leaves the dogma of the distinction of the natures intact. In the same way the Gentiles could touch God in his creation and find him, for "he is not far from each one of us, for in him we live and move and have our being." (Acts xvii.27-8.) The whole world, ourselves included, is indeed his tangible presence.

Where Wisdom is presented in the Old Testament as a person, she is declared to have been involved in the creation of the world as the creative knowledge of God, a knowledge which enables God to bring the order and multiplicity of creatures into being. (Prov. viii.27-9.) Thus Wisdom shares in God's lordship over creation. Indeed, it is God's creative wisdom. God exercises his dominion through his creative wisdom. Wisdom shares in this dominion because it is the creative knowledge of God. She, too, possesses royal power: "I dwelt in high places, and my throne was in a pillar of cloud." (Ecclus. xxiv.4.) "By me kings reign."

(Prov. viii.15.) In the Book of Wisdom, Wisdom is represented as a queen, seated with God on a throne. (ix.4.) She *knows* the works of God and was present when he created the world. (ix.9.) She is the *maker* of all things. (vii.21.) "She glorifies her noble birth by living with God, and the Lord of all *loves* her. For she is an initiate in the *knowledge* of God, and an associate in his *works*." (viii.3-4.) Here the combination of knowing and loving comes to the fore once again, since these together constitute the royal dominion of Wisdom. When we project the line through to the New Testament, we arrive at John v.19-20: "The Son can do nothing of his own accord, but only what he sees the Father doing; for whatever he does, that the Son does likewise. For the Father loves the Son, and shows him all that he himself is doing."

Man shares in Wisdom. We find this thought everywhere in the Wisdom literature. The descriptions of the divine Wisdom in her creative function have for their purpose the illumination of the ordering of human life:

> With thee is wisdom who knows thy works
> and was present when thou didst make the
> world,
> and who understands what is pleasing in thy
> sight
> and what is right according to thy command-
> ments.
> Send her forth from the holy heavens,

and from the throne of thy glory send her,
that she may be with me and toil,
and that I may learn what is pleasing to thee.
[Wisd. of Sol. ix.9-10]

For man wisdom consists in knowing and doing the will of God. Through Wisdom man knows what God's creative will is for him. Creative Wisdom, through which the universe exists, creates man also by means of the inward light of reason directed to God, and shows how to fulfil the commandments in everyday life. For the moment we are particularly interested in the dominion over creation which man possesses because of the wisdom that is in him. We have already spoken about this dominion in connection with Gen. i and ii. Here we also recall the teaching of the Fourth Gospel concerning Jesus as the light of the world. All this is comprehended in Ps. xxxvi.9: "In thy light do we see light." Through the inner light that God gives to men, the creation, too, is illuminated. Physical sunlight becomes light only for those whose life is from God. For the others, the world remains wrapped in darkness, even though God permits the sun to rise over them.

God is sovereign over the universe by virtue of his creative knowing of it. This creative knowing is his wisdom. Wisdom is also portioned out to man, who in turn becomes lord of creation through the knowledge which he possesses. For the continuity of the Old with the New Testament concepts of man as the image of God, and the lord of creation, Ps. viii is particularly important. I give it in its entirety.

O Lord, our Lord,
how majestic is thy name in all the earth!

Thou whose glory above the heavens is chanted
by the mouth of babes and infants,
thou hast founded a bulwark because of thy
  foes,
to still the enemy and the avenger.

When I look at thy heavens, the work of thy
  fingers,
the moon and the stars which thou hast established;
what is man that thou art mindful of him,
and the son of man that thou dost care for him?

Yet thou hast made him little less than God,
and dost crown him with glory and honour.
Thou hast given him dominion over the works
  of thy hands;
thou hast put all things under his feet,
all sheep and oxen,
and also the beasts of the field,
the birds of the air, and the fish of the sea,
whatever passes along the paths of the sea.

O Lord, our Lord,
how majestic is thy name in all the earth!

In this psalm a godly Israelite is speaking who feels how small he is when he views the wonders of the universe. He does not feel small when comparing himself with the great things that surround him, but in relation to God who reveals himself to him in the wonders of creation. But God has called man in his smallness to share in the divine lordship over the universe. Hence the psalmist sees man "robed" in the majesty of an almost divine kingship. The dominion of man over creation is described in terms of Gen. i. Man is great because, as image of God, he rules over things by his knowledge, which is the same knowledge by which he sees the heavens to be the work of God.

The psalm is so important because *v.* 7b, "thou hast put all things under his feet," is applied to Christ in various parts of the New Testament. In Heb. ii.5-9 no less than three verses of the psalm are quoted and given a christological interpretation. The application to Christ is not arbitrary, because the dominion which man has received at his creation is actualized in a new manner in the man Christ. *The divine Wisdom which previously kindled the light in every human heart has now appeared personally in one man.* The incarnation of the divine Wisdom means that a new light has arisen in creation. At this point, in Christ, a human knowledge has entered such as there never was before. The divine Wisdom itself, which is the creative knowing of God, communicates itself personally to the human understanding of Jesus. Hence man becomes king of creation in an entirely new way.

Let us consider 1 Cor. xv.25-8, one of the texts in which

Ps. xiii.7 is quoted. "For he must reign until he has put all his enemies under his feet. [Ps. cx.i.] The last enemy to be destroyed is death. *'For God has put all things in subjection under his feet.'* [Ps. viii.7.] But when it says, 'all things are put in subjection under him,' it is plain that he is excepted who put all things under him. When all things are subjected to him, then the Son himself will also be subjected to him who put all things under him, that God may be everything to everyone."

The thought of Paul is this, that two consecutive subjections take place. One has already occurred, namely the subjection of all things to Christ by his elevation to the right hand of God. It is true that this dominion must yet be carried through until the last enemy is destroyed, but this does not diminish the fact that Christ exercises the lordship. Christ will exercise the lordship until the second subjection takes place. Then there will be a subjection to God of all things, including Christ. The first subjection is thus acted out between Christ and all things, and the second between God and all things, including Christ. In the second subjection Christ subjects himself to God, that God may be *all in all*.

In *vv.* 27-8, from the moment that Ps. viii.7 is quoted, *ta panta,* all things, are mentioned six times. In Ps. viii.7 this refers to "the works of thy hands," thus, to all creatures, and no reason can be given why this should not be so in I Cor. xv. God has subjected the creation, the whole of things, to Christ. The translation "the whole of things," "the universe," is very adequate for *ta panta,* but at the sixth appearance of the expression we start back from this translation. This is not consistent, because the preceding verses are directed precisely to the conclusion of the pericope, "that God may be *everything* to every one." If we everywhere translate *ta panta* by "the universe" then we get: "For God has put the universe in subjection under his [Christ's] feet. But when it says, the universe is put in subjection, it is plain that he [God] is excepted who put all things under him [Christ]. When all things are subjected to him [Christ], then the Son himself will also be subjected to Him who put all things under him, so that God may be the universe in every one."

The lordship of Christ over the universe, actualized in the first subjection, consists in this, that in Christ, the creative knowing of God manifests itself in a human understanding. The lordship of the divine Wisdom which, as creative Wisdom, knows the works of God, is incarnated in Christ, the heavenly man. By this act, man becomes lord of the universe in a new way. God has appointed man anew over the works of his hands. Here is a man who knows the creation, and therefore rules it by the light of the divine wisdom. "And before him no creature is hidden, but all are open and laid bare to his eyes." (Heb. iv.13.) But as long as death is not yet destroyed, that is, while men have not yet passed over into the eternal life of the resurrection, this lordship is confined to Christ. But Christ will duly destroy death and communicate perfected salvation to all who are his. This is the last work which he will do as Saviour. With this, God's will to save will be fulfilled in Christ and in the people who belong to him. God will then reign through Christ over all the saved. Then God will be the universe to everybody, which is to say that God, who rules the universe with his creative knowing, will communicate the light of his creative Wisdom to all who are saved, so that God, in the light which he grants them, will *be the universe* in the saved, insofar as he expresses himself by his creative knowing in the universe. The sanctified will see the universe as the Creator sees it.

"Yet for us there is one God, the Father, from whom are all things and for whom we exist, and one Lord, Jesus Christ, through whom are all things and through whom we exist." (1 Cor. viii.6.) Here also there is mention of two relations. God creates the universe through Jesus Christ, and also Christians through Jesus Christ. They share in the position which Jesus Christ has in respect of the universe.

This sharing in the light of Christ is, for the Christian on earth, still a matter of faith. The Christian knows that in principle Christ has overcome death, but *he does not yet see* the dominion of Christ over all things, and he does not share it yet. The author of Hebrews brings this out in his commentary on Ps. viii.5-7: "Now in putting everything in subjection to him, he left nothing outside his control. As it is, we do not yet see everything in subjection to him." (Heb. ii.8.)

We can pull together what has been said by going over to

the view of the Church in the Letter to the Ephesians. "God is all things [the universe]" is the same thought that we encounter in Jer. xxiii.24: Yahweh fills heaven and earth. God fills the universe with his creative knowing. He who sees the universe sees God in a veiled manner. Seen from God's side this means that the universe is creatively transparent to God, in the first creation, and now, in the second creation; in the first creation through his wisdom, in the second creation through Christ, the First-born, who enters the world afresh. (Heb. i.6.) In the first creation through the Wisdom in which man is given his share, by virtue of which man recognizes the creation as God's creation, and rules over it. (Ps. viii.) Ps. viii is now applied to Christ. Wisdom and man are united in Christ. Wisdom, by which God knows the universe creatively, becomes in Christ incarnate Wisdom. The creative knowing of the universe, which has its origin in God, communicates itself to the understanding of Christ, and through Christ to the understanding of the sanctified. In the sanctified God knows the universe creatively. He is "all things" in them. In them he fills heaven and earth. In man the universe is the *pleroma,* the fullness of God.

By this road we arrive at the special terminology of Ephesians and Colossians, where the expressions "fill up," "the fullness of Christ," "the fullness of God," repeatedly occur. The most important text in this connection is undoubtedly Eph. i.22-3. In the section that precedes these verses, the Apostle prays that God should grant to the faithful the Spirit of wisdom and revelation, so that they may truly know Christ, and see how rich is the glory of his portion among the saints, and how magnified his power is in those who believe. The power of God, which operates in the faithful, is the same as the power by which Christ is raised from the dead, and placed at the right hand of God, above all creatures. And he has put all things under his feet and has made him the head over all things for the Church, which is his body, the fullness (*pleroma*) of him who fills all in all. (Eph. i.22-3.) In every believer and in the whole Church Christ lives as he who fills the universe. "He who descended is he who also ascended far above all the heavens, that he might fill all things" (Eph. iv.10); and it is as such that he is the head of the Church. That is why Christ fills the Church in a special manner, which shares, indeed, in the light of Christ. She is the Body of Christ, his special *pleroma,* because Christ enlightens the Church with his light: "For once you were darkness, but now you are light in the Lord." (Eph. v.8.) This is the light by which Christ, the one new man (Eph. ii.15), exercises dominion over the universe. The Church shares in the light and in the dominion of Christ, the *pleroma* which he fills with his light, and therefore the place where he rules over the all.

However, we must add to this that on earth the Church possesses only the light of faith. Yet faith nevertheless brings with it a true dominion over the universe. Thus the faithful must strive always after a better knowledge of

Christ, in whom are all the treasures of wisdom and knowledge. (Col. ii.2-3.) In this way the body of Christ is built up "until we all attain to the unity of the faith and of the knowledge of the Son of God, to mature manhood, to the measure of the stature of the fullness of Christ." (Eph. iv.13.) The *pleroma,* the fullness, of Christ, is the body of Christ that realizes itself in the Church. It is the domain where the light of Christ will shine fully when the faithful shall fully possess the light. Every believer must realize the form of Christ in himself so that in this way he may become the *pleroma* of Christ in its full amplitude.

The verse of Eph. iv.13 just quoted is brought into relief by comparison with iv.10 and iv.15, between which it is placed. In iv.10 it is said that Christ "is he who also ascended far above all the heavens, that he might fill all things." Now he, as sovereign, sitting at the right hand of God, has distributed gifts by the appointment of apostles, prophets, evangelists, pastors and teachers, who all have the task "for the equipment of the saints, for the work of ministry, for building up the body of Christ." (*vv.* 11-12.) By virtue of the appointment of these guides and teachers believers have the truth taught to them, so that they are able to serve their neighbours by the light that is in them. Thus the mutual love of the body of Christ is built up. (cf. *v.* 16.) In this way all men, however imperfect and incomplete the knowledge with which they start, become increasingly the *pleroma* of Christ, because his light becomes more and more the light of all. Then they will no longer be misled by every doctrine thought out by cunning men. Now comes *v.* 15: "Rather, speaking the truth in love, we are to grow up in every way [or 'in all things'] into him who is the head, into Christ." Openness to the truth in mutual love will gain for Christians the dominion over the universe, so that Christ, who rose to fill all things, will complete this work through his body, the Church.

The remarkable terminology of the Apostle renders his teaching hard to penetrate. If we put what he says into easier language we get the following picture. The universe, originally created by God through the mediation of his wisdom, is estranged from God by sin. It has become a dark world. Men without God "are darkened in their understanding, alienated from the light of God because of the ignorance that is in them, due to their hardness of heart; they have become callous and have given themselves up to licentiousness, greedy to practise every kind of uncleanness." (iv. 19-20.) If the world is once more to have a future, then the light must shine again in the hearts of men, so that they once more see things as God's creation and restore its destination to the transient world. Man must regain dominion over the universe. God established this dominion in principle when he subjected all things to the Man by elevating Christ to his right hand. The lordship of Christ must now be carried through in the world. This happens in the Church, which shares in the light of Christ. The Church is the place where the universe is daily brought into subjection to Christ by the rule, in Christians, of the spirit over the flesh, and the light cast upon things by their mutual love.

Christians on earth do not yet possess the fullness of light. Christ already fulfils the universe in them, but the Christian himself lives all this out only in faith. Christ reigns in the believer through the creative knowledge of God which is in him. That is why the Christian is already known by Christ, though the Christian has not yet knowledge of Christ save by faith. Christ lives in his heart by faith (iii.7): "For now we see in a mirror dimly, but then face to face. Now I know in part; then I shall understand fully, *even as I have been fully understood.*" (1 Cor. xiii.12.) The vision face to face refers to the knowledge which the Christian will have of Christ after this life. Just as God now and already knows him in Christ, so the Christian will know God in Christ. The light of Christ coalesces with the light in every saint, so that in the domain of Christ's kingdom there will be only one new Man, not in such a way that the saints will lose their individuality, but because they will know with the knowledge of Christ. Then only will they know who Christ is; because they are in him, and in him and with him rule over the universe.

But the infinity of the invisible God will for ever be inaccessible to the sanctified. In his absolute transcendence the invisible God has also his *pleroma,* an incommunicable knowledge which is not creative but which expresses itself in the Son. This *pleroma,* called in Col. ii.9 the fullness of the Godhead, *dwells* in a bodily manner in Christ and has become man in Christ. Through the glorified Lord and through the Church the proper *pleroma* of God is translated in a creaturely mode. This translation is the new creation, in which God, through Christ and the Church, fulfils the universe in a new manner, in a way analogous to that in which God, through his *pleroma,* the eternally uncreated Wisdom, filled full the first creation and subjected it to man. Through Christ the faithful enter the *pleroma* of God. They are fulfilled in Christ (Col. ii.9) until the *pleroma* of God is fully realized in them. (Eph. iii.19.)

> Be subject to one another out of reverence for Christ. Wives, be subject to your husbands, as to the Lord. For the husband is the head of the wife as Christ is the head of the church, his body, and is himself its Saviour. As the church is subject to Christ, so let wives also be subject in everything to their husbands. Husbands, love your wives, as Christ loved the church and gave himself up for her, that he might sanctify her, having cleansed her by the washing of water with the word, that he might present the church to himself in splendour, without spot or wrinkle or any such thing, that she might be holy and without blemish. [Eph. v.21-7.]

Mankind becomes the body of Christ, the Church, by baptism, indicated in early Christian writing by the word "enlightenment." (Cf. Heb. vi.4.) God "has qualified us to share in the inheritance of the saints in light. He has delivered us from the dominion of darkness and transferred us to the kingdom of his beloved Son, in whom we have redemption, the forgiveness of sins." (Col. i.12-14.) Baptism leads men into the light of Christ. Christ gave himself over, in order to be the light of men.

Christ is the head of the Church. He is the saviour of his body. The relationship of Head and Body expresses the fact that the light springs up in Christ and is communicated by him to the Church. On the other side Christ is "one flesh" with the Church (v.31-2) precisely through the possession of a common light and life. The risen Lord lives in his own, who have clothed themselves with him in baptism, so that all bear only one form: that of Christ. "For in Christ Jesus you are all sons of God, through faith. For as many of you as were baptised into Christ have put on Christ. There is neither Jew nor Greek, there is neither slave nor free, there is neither male nor female; for you are all one [Man] in Christ Jesus." (Gal. iii.26-8; cf. iii.16: One, which is Christ.)

The glorified Lord himself is thus the primal figure of the Church, and whoever comes to Him through baptism, becomes the Church because he assumes the figure of Christ. Thus does Christ, until the end of time, build up his body, not so that it grows quantitatively, but so that ever more persons are clothed with his form. In this holy place, which is the Church as the body of Christ, the service of baptism is performed. "For by one Spirit we were all baptised into one body—Jews or Greeks, slaves or free—and all were made to drink of one Spirit." (1 Cor. xii.13.)

The immaculate bride of Christ, purified through the baptism of the word, conceives daily by the Holy Spirit, to bear children for eternal life.

# 13

# THE CHRISTIAN LIFE

"Credo in unum baptisma in remissionem peccatorum": "I believe in one baptism for the remission of sins." The Council of Trent[1] defined that in baptism original sin is forgiven, and that everything which, in a true and proper sense, is sin, is removed by baptism. The Council goes on to lay down that concupiscence remains in the baptized. It remains until the agony of death as a testing-ground on which the Christian must battle to receive his crown. It is stated that concupiscence is no sin, but that its roots are in sin, and that it tempts to sin.

Our point of departure was the thesis that the historical fall in paradise, coupled with the loss of an original, paradisal integrity, must be regarded as proclaiming a revelation of the condition of man under God, using an image of a static world. However, what we have been saying preserves the content of the dogma, so that everything which Trent says about baptism is able to come into its own. In this

[1] Denz., 792.

exposition baptism has primarily the character of a new creation. All that counts is a new creation, St. Paul writes to the Galatians. (vi.15.) And in another letter: "Therefore, if anyone is in Christ, he is a new creation; the old has passed away, behold, the new has come." (2 Cor. v.17.) This refers to what is in the most actual sense a creative act of God. Besides this, baptism effects the forgiveness of sins. The plural, sins, indicates that originally baptism was administered to adults, but the plural retains its significance in the baptism of infants. The forgiveness of sins in adults is more than just wiping them off the account in an external way. It is an interior purgation from dead works, by means of which the believer is brought into the service of the living God. (Heb. ix.14.)

Thus forgiveness of sins means interior reorientation, the creation of a new heart. When baptism is administered to newly born infants, they also become a new creature, and their subsequent lives are in principle delivered from the power of sin. Baptism releases the child from sin, even though he has not committed any. But above all, it frees the child so that, by the grace of God, he can complete his creation.

Man is created with the desire for the vision of God, which is signified in his second creation. Or more precisely, his true creation, to which his earthly existence is directed, is that which belongs to the end of time, for then only will man be as God finally wants him to be. Christ, who is assumed into unveiled communion with God, is the Man who crowns evolution, the purpose of the creative work of God. The first creation of man asks for this completion. Christ is the way, and nobody can reach his completion unless he follows this way. It comes to the same thing if we put it that nobody can follow this way except by the grace of Christ. Before the coming of Christ there was, it is true, a way to God, because God was already occupied in leading man to completion by his wisdom, just because he was looking to the salvific work of Christ as the conclusion of the economy of salvation. But the consummation, man's becoming heavenly man, remains unattainable while the creation of the First-born within many brothers has not yet taken place. Even the godly of the Old Covenant "did not receive what was promised, since God had foreseen something better for us." (Heb. xi.39-40.) Only when God has rent the curtain do the graves open and the holy dead arise. (Matt. xxvii.51-2.)

Now that the heavenly man has become actual, the way to the end lies open. Man, created as openness to God without being able to actualize this disposition in his own strength, can now be assumed into the new creation for which he was intended. It is true that he continues to live in the flesh, and that in all his ways of behaviour he remains the man of earth; yet by baptism all this is assumed into a new orientation beyond nature, which the Spirit of the heavenly man creates in him. The earthly life of the Christian differs in no way from that of other people, except for this orientation and this light, by means of which the Christian is enabled by God to rule over the flesh and the things of the world and to prepare himself for his transformation into the heavenly man, which will be his lot at death. Just as, when he came into being, an orientation to God was inscribed in this being, so in his baptism he is already touched by the heavenly man. His becoming a child of God is a new creation, which may well be deformed, but which can never be undone. Just as man is in his essence a seeking for God, and he thus possesses this capacity long before he becomes conscious of it, so the newly born child receives his new creation in the shape of a supernatural directedness to God long before he witnesses to it in life.

The Christian attitude to life must, according to the preaching of Jesus, always preserve the receptivity of the child. When Jesus proposes the child to the adult as an example, it is because the child is still in a condition of unprejudiced receptivity: "Let the children come to me, do not hinder them; for to such belongs the kingdom of God. Truly, I say to you, whoever does *not receive the kingdom of God like a child* shall not enter it." (Mark i.14-15.) Elsewhere Jesus says: "I thank thee, Father, Lord of heaven and earth, that thou hast hidden these things from the wise and understanding and revealed them to babes." (Matt. xi.25.) The babes here are adults, the disciples who have received the word of Jesus and learned to know him as he who reveals the Father. In this the disciples displayed the openness of the child.

In this context the teaching about the giving of offence

occurs: "Whoever causes one of these little ones who believe in me to sin, it would be better for him if a great millstone were hung round his neck and he were thrown into the sea." (Mark ix.42.) The uninhibitedness of the child makes it dependent on its surroundings, which can affect it for good or evil. Hence it is a most serious matter if the adult in any manner exposes the receptivity of the child to offence. The existence of the child cannot be abstracted from his surroundings. Just as for physical well-being he is dependent on adults, so for spiritual development he is bound up with the community in which he is born and reborn. Thus baptism is not merely a transaction between God and the child, but also puts the child into the sacred space of the Church, which is necessary to the living out of his supernatural orientation to God which is given in baptism. Baptism withdraws the child from the world as the domain of the enemy. It frees the child from the compulsive power of sin.

Thus does the Christian enter upon life, led by the light of faith. Although the earthly body defines the area in which the Christian, too, must be active in the world, in the company of all the others who have the same level of existence, yet he possesses a re-created orientation to God, and an insight which definitively transforms his power of valuation. He travels a way which nobody can traverse without the light of faith, a way which cannot be comprehended by the outsider. "The reason why the world does not know us is that it did not know him." (1 John iii.1.)

The course of life of the Christian is sketched beforehand by Jesus. From the Synoptic Gospels, especially the Gospel according to Mark, it appears that the public actions of Jesus confronted the Jews with a problem. Mark shows more clearly than the other Evangelists how the disciples gradually began to comprehend something of the person of Jesus, while the crowd failed to do so. The actions of Jesus did not correspond to what men expected of the Messiah. The Jewish expectation of the Kingdom of God and the Messiah, as it comes to the surface here and there in the Gospels (Mark viii.32; x.37; xi.10; Luke xix.11; xxii.38; xxiii.42; xxiv.21; John vi.15) and which related to restoration of Israel's earthly fortunes, on the religious as well as the political level, separates along two lines in the person of Jesus. The one line is inferior, the other superior to the established expectation of salvation, but the two lines are united in the ministry of Jesus. On the one hand, the ministry of Jesus is a great disappointment to those who expect a Messiah who will restore the Kingdom of Israel, because the behaviour of Jesus is marked by a desire to remain hidden from those who live in this expectation. On the other hand, Jesus is the veiled revelation of a transcendent personality: the beholder has to see through his humble human form and discover the Son of God in him. Here, and to the eye of faith, a dimension of the Kingdom is revealed which far surpasses expectation. Jesus' appearance is at one and the same time a revelation of what he actually is and the veiling of his true identity by an attitude of service ending in the downfall of death. Any recognition of the Messiah which does not embrace both aspects of his course must on that account be rejected.

The first part of the Gospel according to Mark culminates in the confession of Peter, "You are the Christ." (Mark viii.29.) Without doubt this confession contains the recognition of Christ's transcendent personality, as the account of Matthew clearly relates: "You are the Christ, the Son of the living God." (Matt. xvi.16.) From that moment Christ begins to explain to his disciples in all clarity that he must walk the road of the Servant of Yahweh: "And he began to teach them that the Son of man must suffer many things, and be rejected by the elders and the chief priests and the scribes, and be killed, and after three days arise again." (Mark viii.31; cf. ix.12; ix.31; x.33-4; x.45; xiv.41.)

In this image of Christ, which the disciples found so hard to comprehend, we also have in view the behaviour of Christians. The highest revelation of God in our world of earth, the place where God in his Son most nearly approaches man, is the figure of service in which the Son of God manifests himself to the world. When incarnate Wisdom, engaged in the creation of the new man, shows only humble service to his neighbour, all who wish to share in the new creation in him know that they must travel by the same road, against the current of human wisdom. Just as Jesus for his contemporaries, so Christians true to their vocation must be a problem to puzzle the contemporary world, and if not to puzzle, then to offend.

Paul speaks about this in his first Letter to the Corinthians: "For the work of the cross is folly to those who are perishing, but to us who are being saved it is the power of God. For it is written, 'I will destroy the wisdom of the wise, and the cleverness of the clever I will thwart.' Where is the wise man? Where is the scribe? Where is the debater of this age? Has not God made foolish the wisdom of this world? For since, in the wisdom of God, the world did not know God through wisdom, it pleased God through the folly of what we preach to save those who believe. For Jews demand signs, and Greeks seek wisdom, but we preach Christ crucified, a stumbling block to Jews and folly to Gentiles, but to those who are called, both Jews and Greeks, Christ the power of God and the wisdom of God. For the foolishness of God is wiser than men, and the weakness of God is stronger than men. For consider your call, brethren; not many of you were wise according to worldly standards, not many were powerful, not many were of noble birth; but God chose what is foolish in the world to shame the wise, God chose what is weak in the world to shame the strong, God chose what is low and despised in the world, even things that are not, to bring to nothing things that are, so that no human being might boast in the presence of God." (1 Cor. i.18-29.)

We could refer here to the Sermon on the Mount, where Jesus presents a way of behaviour which must count as foolishness in the eyes of a world living according to its own insights. This is particularly true where Jesus speaks of loving our enemies. Here we are at the heart of the Gospel: "Love your enemies and pray for those who persecute you, so that you may be sons of your Father who is in heaven; for he makes his sun rise on the evil and on the good, and sends rain on the just and on the unjust. For if you love those who love you, what reward have you? Do not even the tax-collectors do the same? And if you salute only your brethren, what more are you doing than others? Do not even the Gentiles do the same? You, therefore, must be perfect, as your heavenly Father is perfect." (Matt. v.44-8.)

Jesus himself preceded us on this way. It is here that it most clearly appears that the work of salvation is a work of creation. He who knows love only as the response to love does no more than the Gentiles can do. But he who shows love to his enemy creates love where it did not previously exist. In Rom. v.5-8 Paul gives the assurance that the hope of Christians in the coming glory will not be disappointed, because the love which God bears them appears from the gift of the Holy Spirit: "Hope does not disappoint us, because God's love has been poured into our hearts through the Holy Spirit which has been given to us. While we were yet helpless, at the right time Christ died for the ungodly. Why, one will hardly die for a righteous man—though perhaps for a good man one will dare even to die. But God shows his love for us in that while we were yet sinners Christ died for us." The love of God for Christians is here drawn in terms of its manifestation in Christ, a point which comes out especially in the last sentence of the passage quoted. In the death which Christ suffered for sinners, God has shown his love. Christ died for the helpless, for sinners, those who, further on, in *v.* 10, are called "enemies." "While we were enemies we were reconciled to God." God's love in Christ is creative, because it overcomes enmity. This love supports the Christian and manifests itself in him through the presence of the Spirit.

Thus there comes to birth in the Christian, too, a creative love which overcomes enmity. It is the continuation of the love revealed in Jesus' earthly life and especially in his death on the Cross. True Christianity reveals itself in this victorious love. To this love, which is sovereign in the Church, the future of the world is entrusted.

At his creation man received the commission to till the earth and care for it. From the dim times of prehistory until deep into the historical period he has done this in a sort of subjection to a nature whose obstinacy has continually threatened his existence. In recent times the relation of man to nature has been radically altered. The discovery of the laws of nature and their application in technics have largely freed him from his subjection. The toilsome tilling of the earth is going to belong to the past, but it is more clear than ever that the other part of his commission, the conservation of the earth, is going to claim his full attention. It is not an unreal question, whether man, in the near future, will succeed in this.

The unbeliever who looks at the course of evolution, especially of human evolution, can give no certain answer to this question. For such a person the probability will appear to be No rather than Yes. There have always been wars: we must thus expect that there will be wars in the future. Weapons are being perfected, and the number of casualties increases. The time is not far distant when the destructive consequences of war will be able to reduce the world's population to a very small percentage, which will consist of people who carry the seeds of death in them.

The Christian cannot appropriate this sombre image of the future. He believes in a future for the world which has been granted to us as a possibility by God in Christ. It is precisely in these times that the Church must show herself for what she is: the bearer of the light of Christ. There is no other power on earth which can fend off the coming evil than she who possesses the light which will subject nature to man. The way to this is not a strategical deployment of strength, but precisely the abandonment of everything resembling human pride of power. Every believer, and the Church as a whole, must follow in the steps of him who did not come to be served but to serve, and to give his life as a ransom for many.

In our century mankind will form a unity unknown before. But the same technical achievement which makes this unification possible reveals itself at the same time to be a power which threatens to escape from human control. The atom bomb hangs over our heads as an enduring menace. Abolition of the bomb is not possible. Even though all stocks were destroyed, the atom bomb would still go on existing in the minds of physicists as a realizable possibility. From now on the world must live with the potentiality of obliterating itself.

This threat to the future of a world which has been entrusted to the care of man must open our eyes, especially those of Christians, to the fact that all of us, dwellers upon the earth, form only one family, and that our preservation depends simply and solely on this, that we be genuine Christians. It is inconceivable how people who call themselves Christians can support racial discrimination. Further, it is not compatible with the teaching of Jesus that the West, which calls itself Christian, should possess the wealth of the world, while it abandons to poverty the remaining eighty per cent of the world's population. There can be a future for the world only if this state of affairs is done away with.

> If you take away from the midst of you the
> yoke,
> the pointing of the finger, and speaking wicked-
> ness,
> if you pour yourself out for the hungry
> and satisfy the desire of the afflicted . . .
> then your ancient ruins shall be rebuilt;
> you shall raise up the foundations of many
> generations;
> you shall be called the repairer of the breach,
> the restorer of streets to dwell in.
>
> [Isa. lviii.9-10, 12]

The word of the prophet is guaranteed by God. We, who live under the Gospel, must interpret this word in the light of the creative love which Jesus brought. We must believe that where politics fail, the foolishness of Christianity will open a new future. The future of the earth depends on sacrificing service and love of our enemies, by which the Christian both enriches himself and protects the world from destruction. This is not merely a hypothesis, but appears to follow necessarily from what we have said, from revelation, about God's creative work. Where there is no subjection to the will of God, God's creative work cannot be carried through. In earlier days the future of the earth did not depend on this, because disobedient man did not possess the power of annihilation which he has now got for himself. The wickedness of man is now able to make our planet uninhabitable. That will inevitably happen if the day does not dawn in which love overcomes enmity.

It is incomprehensible why assistance to underdeveloped areas should be coloured by political and economic considerations and that this assistance should be limited to non-hostile countries. If we act in this way we still fall quite short of the foolishness of being Christians, in which the creative wisdom of God asserts itself. We are also far from having arrived at the Christian joy in the detachment which knows that the Kingdom of God does not consist in eating and drinking (Rom. xiv.17), and at the knowledge of God in that love which becomes actual only when we really *share* what we have with our fellow man. Greater sacrifices are now asked from Christians than were asked in the past. Christians must feel themselves the more responsible for the future of the world in the measure in which the world grows towards unity, and the common destiny of all comes home to each personally. New and unheard-of things must happen. Our neighbour who is poor no longer lives in our city or in our country, but in our world. What the Gospel says about our attitude to the poor and to our enemies we have to carry out nowadays at world level. This is what the world's future depends upon.

The people asked John the Baptist: "What then shall we do?" And he answered them, "He who has two coats, let him share with him who has none; and he who has food, let him do likewise." (Luke iii.10-11.) "For you know the grace of our Lord Jesus Christ, that though he was rich, yet for your sake he became poor, so that by his poverty you might become rich. For if the readiness is there, it is acceptable according to what a man has, not according to what he has not. I do not mean that others should be eased and you burdened, but that as a matter of equality your abundance at the present time should supply their want, that there may be equality. And it is written, 'He who gathered much had nothing over, and he who gathered little had no lack.'" (2 Cor. viii. 9, 12-15.) "If your enemy is hungry, feed him; for by so doing you will heap burning coals upon his head. Do not be overcome by evil but overcome evil with good." (Rom. xii.20-21.)

Not only by means of material assistance to the needy,

but also by a genuine *openness to the Truth* which alone can set us free, must Christians assure the world's future. Let us, holding to the truth in love, let all things grow towards him. The witness of Jesus is not audible when a divided Christendom interprets it. The Churches will have to find each other in the true evangelical form of service to one's neighbour, and in listening to each other with the uninhibitedness of the child. They will have to refrain from any use of power which is not "the power of the cross." (1 Cor. i.17.) I believe that the Catholic Church would take a decisive step in furthering the unity of Christians, and therefore towards the saving of the world, were she to remove from her outward form whatever reminds us of political power. Other churches, who do not understand this side, may otherwise suffer from an unevangelical urge toward self-preservation, and thus be hindered in their openness to truth.

We shall have to give our lives to find them again, for ourselves and those who come after.

# EPILOGUE

*Revelation iii.14-22*

The words of the Amen, the faithful and true witness, *the beginning of God's creation.*

"I know your works: you are neither cold nor hot. Would that you were cold or hot! So, because you are lukewarm, and neither cold nor hot, I will spew you out of my mouth. For you say, I am rich, I have prospered, and I need nothing; not knowing that you are wretched, pitiable, poor, blind, and naked. Therefore I counsel you to buy from me gold refined by fire, that you may be rich, and white garments to clothe you and to keep the shame of your nakedness from being seen, and salve to anoint your eyes, that you may see. Those whom I love, I reprove and chasten; so be zealous and repent. Behold, I stand at the door and knock; if any one hears my voice and opens the door, I will come in to him and eat with him, and he with me. He who conquers, I will grant him to sit with me on my throne, as I myself conquered and sat down with my Father on his throne. He who has an ear, let him hear what the Spirit says to the churches."

# INDEX

# INDEX